Basics of
Agriculture for Engineers

The Authors

Mr. Rakesh Kumar Sharma is Assistant Seed Certification Officer in CGSSCA, Raipur. He has also worked as Senior Surveillance Inspector and SRF in Indira Gandhi Krishi Vishwavidyalaya, Raipur. He received his B.Sc (Ag.) in 2006 and M.Sc (Ag.) degree in 2008 in the field of Agronomy from Indira Gandhi Krishi Vishwavidyalaya, Raipur (C.G.). He has qualified JRF (Agronomy) during 2006 and Ph.D. Exams of Banaras Hindu University and GBPUAT during 2009-10 and NET (ICAR) examination during 2010. He has published books "**Guide for Agricultural Entrance Examinations**" "**Agriculture At A Glance**" and "**Question Bank For Agricultural Examinations**", many research papers and technical articles. He has lot of experience of teaching of Under-graduate programme.

Mr. A.K. Soni is working as a Rural Agriculture Extension Officer at Pathariya (Mungeli District). He has worked as Block Technology Manager in Kanker district (C.G.). He received his B.Sc. (Ag.) in 2006 and M.Sc. (Ag.) degree in 2008 in the field of Horticulture from IGKV, Raipur (C.G.)

Mr. Ram Chandra Bhagat is working as a Rural Agriculture Extension Officer at Katghora (Korba District). He has also worked as Senior Research Fellow in Dept. of Soil Science and Agricultural Chemistry, IGKV, Raipur (C.G.). He received his B.Sc. (Ag.) in 2007 and M.Sc. (Ag.) degree in 2010 in the field of Soil Science from IGKV, Raipur (C.G.).

Dr. N. Pandey Principal Scientist in the Department of Agronomy, Indira Gandhi Krishi Vishwavidyalaya, Raipur. He received his B.Sc. (Ag.) and M.Sc. (Ag.) degree from Jawahar Lal Nehru Krishi Vishwavidyalaya, Jabalpur and Ph.D. from Indian Institute of Technology, Kharagpur. He is well known for his work on water and nutrient management and cropping system. He has published and presented more than 150 research papers in different journals and many technical bulletins for providing technologies to the farmers. He has vast experience of teaching of Under-graduate, Post-graduate and Ph.D. programme, and research and extension activities. He has published the book "Guide for Agricultural Entrance Examinations" and "Agriculture At A Glance" as co-author. At present, he is the Principal Scientist of All India Co-ordinated Rice Improvement Project in the Department of Agronomy, IGKV, Raipur.

Dr. V.K. Pandey is Professor and Incharge Dean of BRSM College of Agril. Engineering and Technology Mungeli, IGKV, Raipur. He is M.E. and Ph.D. in Agricultural Engineering from Indian Institute of Technology, Kharagpur. He has published and presented more than 56 research papers in various International and National journals, Conference proceedings etc. He has an experience of about 22 years in teaching, research and extension activity in the field of his specialization.

Basics of
Agriculture for Engineers

Useful for B.Tech. (Agricultural Engineering)

Edited and Compiled by
R.K. Sharma
&
A.K.Soni, R. Bhagat, N. Pandey and V.K. Pandey

2014
Daya Publishing House®
A Division of
Astral International Pvt. Ltd.
New Delhi – 110 002

Published by : **Daya Publishing House®**
A Division of
Astral International Pvt. Ltd.
– ISO 9001:2008 Certified Company –
4760-61/23, Ansari Road, Darya Ganj
New Delhi-110 002
Ph. 011-43549197, 23278134
E-mail: info@astralint.com
Website: www.astralint.com

Laser Typesetting : **Classic Computer Services**, Delhi - 110 035

Printed at : **Replika Press Pvt. Ltd.**

PRINTED IN INDIA

Preface

Agricultural Engineering is the engineering discipline that applies engineering science and technology to agricultural production and processing. Agricultural engineering has been accepted as one of the major disciplines which contribute significantly in increasing the productivity of agriculture in the country by way of increasing efficiency of inputs, conservation of resources and reducing post harvest losses besides value addition of agro-produce. Basically there are four major specializations in agricultural engineering namely, farm machinery and power engineering, irrigation and drainage engineering soil and water conservation engineering, post harvest process and food engineering. Agriculture Engineers must have the knowledge of Agriculture to perform the services in the field of research, extension and academics.

The book entitled "Basics of Agriculture for Engineers" is a scientific approach for understanding of the problems concerning soil, plants, agricultural equipments and their management for augmenting agricultural production on a sustained basis. The problem encountered may be of varied nature requiring for proper diagnosis and remedial measures. An attempt has been made to explain the fundamentals in a simple, lucid language. Basic concepts have been emphasized throughout. This book covers all the topics related to Agronomy, Soil Science and Horticulture.

The authors are highly thankful to all teachers and scientists for their kind co-operation towards speedy preparation of this publication. Authors are also indebted to all friends and colleagues who have helped them at every stage of the preparation of this book. Though every care has been taken to avoid any misprint, omission and errors; yet the same might have left in due to oversight. Authors will, personally thank the person who brings to his notice and shortcoming and the same will be taken care of, for the future edition of this book to make it more useful for the students and readers.

R.K. Sharma

Contents

Chapter 1
Soil Science

(A) Definition and Origin of Soil

☆ The word **"Soil"** is derived from Latin word **'Solum'** means **'Floor'** or **'Ground'**.

Definition of Soil

1. "Soil is a natural body composed of inorganic and organic constituents, having a definite genesis and a distinct nature of its own"— **Dokuchalev (1900).**

2. "Soil is a natural occurring body that has been evolved owing to combined influence of climate and other organisms, acting on parent material, as conditioned by relief over a period of time".

3. "Soil is the unconsolidated mineral matter on the immediate surface of the earth that serves as a natural medium for the growth of land plants".

Soil Components

Soil consists of **four major components** *i.e.*, inorganic or mineral materials, organic matter, water and air. In a representative loam surface soil, **the solid mineral particles comprise about 45 per cent of the soil volume and organic matter 5 per cent.** At optimum moisture for plant growth, the pore space is divided roughly in half, **25 per cent, of volume being water space and 25 per cent air**. The proportions of air and water are subjected to rapid and great fluctuations. The four soil components occur in a thoroughly mixed condition in soil and this mixture encourages interactions with in and between the groups and permits marked variations in the environment for the growth of plants. The proportion of different components in the diagram depicts the good soil condition for plant growth. The air and water are extremely variable and their proportions determine in large degree the soil's suitability for the plant growth.

a) **Mineral Matter**: The Inorganic portion of soils is quite variable in size and composition. It is composed of small rock fragments and minerals of various kinds.

- ❖ Rock Fragments:

    2.0 - 75.0 mm - Gravel or pebbles

    75.0 - 250.0 mm - Cobbles (round), flags (flat)

    > 250.0 mm - Stones or boulders

- ❖ Soil Particles:

    0.2 - 2.0 mm - Course Sand (gritty)

    0.02 - 0.2mm - Fine sand (gritty)

    0.002 - 0.02 mm - Silt (powdery)

    < 0.002mm - Clay (sticky)

    The proportion of different sized particles (texture) determines the nutrient supplying power of the soil, considerably. Primary minerals (original) are prominent in sand and slit fractions; where as the secondary minerals (formed) dominate in clay fraction and in some cases the silt fraction. The inorganic fraction of soil is the original source of most of the mineral elements that are essential for plant growth.

- ❖ **Primary minerals:** Feldspar, Quartz, Mica, Limestone, Hornblende, augite, Olivine and serpentine.

- ❖ **Secondary minerals:**

    1:1 – One silica and one alumina layer: Kaolinite, Halloysite and Dickite.

    2:1 – Two silica and one alumina layer: Montmorillonite, Vermiculite and Illite.

    2:1:1 or 2:2 – The crystal unit is composed of one 2:1 unit: Chlorite.

- ❖ Accessory minerals: Tourmaline, Topaz, Apatite, Rutile and Anatase.

- ❖ Amorphous minerals: Allophane.

b) **Organic Matter:** It comprises an accumulation of partially disintegrated and decomposed plant and animal residues and other organic compounds synthesized by soil microbes as the decay occurs.

    It is a transitory soil constituent as it is continuously broken down by soil organisms and lasts from few hours to several hundred years. It requires maintenance by regular addition to the soil of plant and/or animal residues. Organic matter content varies from 1.0 to 6.0 per cent by weight in top soil and very less in sub soil. In respect of soil productivity organic matter plays an indispensable role.

- ❖ Decomposition of organic matter by humidification process gives humus.

❖ In hilly and high altitudes areas, OM is above 1 per cent.

❖ CN ratio of OM is 10:1, whereas an average of 14:1 of Indian soil.

❖ Histosols are called Organic soils.

c) **Soil Water:** Soil water is held in soil pores with varying degrees of tenacity depending on the amount of water present and size of the pores. Soil water with its soluble constituents (nutrients) makes up soil solution, which is the critical medium for supplying nutrients to growing plants. Soil water plays significant role in controlling energy balance of the soil and regulates the gaseous exchange in the upper layer of the soil. The presence of water in different amounts in soil governs its thermal, mechanical, physical, chemical and biological properties.

d) **Soil Air:** The content and composition of soil air are determined largely by the water content of the soil, since the air occupies those soil pores not filled with water. Soil air always differs from atmosphere air in composition because of moisture content, root and microbial activities.

Branches of Soil Science

1. **Pedology:** The Science dealing with the genesis,survey and classification and the laws of geographical distribution of soils as a body in nature. Pedology is the study of soil as a natural body and does not focus primarily on the soil's immediate practical use.

2. **Edaphology:** The science that deals with the influence of soils on living things, particularly plants, including man's use of land for plant growth. Edaphology is the study of soil from the stand point of higher plants.

3. **Soil Fertility:** The quality of the soil that enables it to provide essential chemical elements in quantities and proportions for the growth of specified plants.

4. **Soil Chemistry:** Deals with the chemical constituents, the chemical properties and the chemical reactions of soil in relation to crop needs.

5. **Soil Physics:** Study of various physical processes that are taking place in and through the soils.

6. **Soil Microbiology:** Deals with microscopic population of the soil, its role in various transformations and its importance in plant nutrition and crop production.

7. **Soil Conservation:** Deals with the protection of soil against physical loss by erosion and against chemical deterioration.

8. **Soil Genesis:** The study of the mode of origin of soils, with special reference to the processes responsible for the development of Solum or true soil from the unconsolidated parent material.

9. **Soil Survey:** The systematic examination, description, classification and mapping of soils in an area.

(B) Rocks and Minerals

☆ The materials of earths crust are nothing but rocks and minerals. These are the out come of the geological forces or processes which operate on the surface and the interior of the earth to bring about changes to produce rocks.

Rocks

Rock may be defined as a hard mass of mineral matter comprising two or more rock forming minerals.

1. Earth crust is made-up of Igneous rocks (**95 per cent)** and Sedimentary rocks (**5 per cent).**

2. In upper 5 km of earth crust, Igneous rocks (18 per cent), Sedimentary rocks (74 per cent) and others (8 per cent) exist.

Formation of Rocks

The various processes that lead to the formation of rocks are:

(A) **Cooling and consolidation of Magma:** Rocks are formed by cooling and consolidation of molten magma with in or on the surface of the earth *e.g.* **igneous or primary rocks**. (Magma is defined as the complex hot solution of silicates containing water vapour and gases having a temperature ranging from 700–1400°C and originating at great depths in the earth crust.)

e.g. Igneous Rocks : Granite, Basalt and Syenite

(B) **Transportation and Cementation of Fragmentary Material:** Disintegration and decomposition lead to the breaking down of pre-existing rocks. The resulting fragmentary material is either compacted *in situ* or transported in solution by the natural agencies of wind, water and ice to low lying areas like oceans. Consolidation of these materials after their deposition results in the formation of rocks called **sedimentary or secondary rocks.**

Sedimentary Rocks : Lime stone, Sand stone and Dolomite

(C) **Alteration of Pre-existing rocks:** The primary and secondary rocks when subjected to earth's movement and to high temperature and pressure are partially or wholly reconstituted or altered to new rocks called **metamorphic rocks.**

Metamorphic rocks: Gneiss, Marble, Quartzite and Slate (Gneiss from Granite, Marble from Lime stone, Quartzite from Sand stone and Slate from Shales).

Minerals

Mineral is a naturally occurring, homogenous element or inorganic compound that has a definite chemical composition and a characteristic geometric form.

Classification of Minerals

(A) *Primary Minerals*

The primary minerals are those which are formed owing to the crystallization of the molten magma. Depending up on the tetrahedral linkage, the silicate minerals are divided in to four groups. The examples are:

1. Orthosilicates : Olivine
2. Inosilicates :
   a. Single chained : Pyroxenes
   b. Double chained : Ampliboles
3. Phyllosilicates : Biotite, Muscovite
4. Tectosilicates : Quartz, Feldspars
5. Ferro - Magnesium Minerals : Olivines, Pyroxenes, Amphiboles, Biotite
6. Non Ferro Magnesian Minerals : Muscovite, Orthoclase, Albite, Anorthite, Quartz

PRIMARY SILICATE MINERALS

1) **Quartz:** The frame works of quartz is very densely packed and occurs in a high degree of purity. It is resistant to physical and chemical weathering as the structure is densely packed electrically neutral and prevents any form of substitution. It is ubiquitous in soils but its abundance is next only to feldspars.

2) **Feldspars:** Its frame work is less dense that quartz. There are most abundant among rock forming minerals in the earth's crust. These are non ferro-magnesium minerals and act as store house of sodium, calcium, potassium minerals and many trace elements in soils.

3) **Micas:** Occur most extensively in soils. Muscovite (white mica) a non-ferromagnesian mineral is resistant for weathering. Biotite (black mica) a ferro-magnesian is highly susceptible for weathering. Muscovite is present only in acid igneous rocks.

4) **Pyroxenes and Amphiboles:** These two minerals are two groups of ferro-magnesium minerals and their structure consists of long chains of linked silica tetrehedra (Inosilicates). Due to variety of substitutions these minerals are excellent host minerals for trace cations in soils and also for main constituent cations like Ca, Mg and Fe. Their weatherability is quite favourable to provide sufficient amounts of these ions in available form for plant nutrition.

   e.g. Pyroxenes - Augite (Single chain)

5) **Olivines:** Olive green colored minerals. Olivines are relatively easily weathered. It is called island silicate. *e.g.* Forsterite and Fayalite

Essential Minerals

The minerals which form the chief constituents of rock and which are regarded as the characteristic components of that rock are known as "Essential Minerals".

    e.g. Quartz, Feldspars and Micas

    ☆ **Accessory Minerals :** These minerals occur only in small quantities and whose presence or absence is of no consequence as far as the character of the rock is concerned, are called as accessory minerals *e.g.* Tourmaline, Pyrite, Magnetite.

    ☆ **Light Minerals:** Are the minerals which have specific gravity below 2.85 g/cc. *e.g.* Quartz (2.60), Feldspar (2.65), Muscovite (2.50-2.75)

    ☆ **Heavy Minerals :** Having specific gravity above 2.85 g/cc. *e.g.* Haematite (5.30), Pyrite (5.0), Limonite (3.8), Augite (pyroxene) (3.1 – 3.6), Olivine (3.5)

(B) Secondary Minerals

The secondary minerals are formed at the earth's surface by the weathering of the pre-existing primary minerals under variable conditions of temperature and pressure. Due to the action of weathering processes primary minerals are altered or decomposed. The examples are:

    1. **Silicates -**

    Clay minerals : Illite, Montmorillonite, Kaolinite

    2. **Non Silicates -**

    Oxides, Hydroxides of Al and Fe : Hematite, Goethite, Gibbsite

    Carbonates: Calcite, Dolomite

    Sulphates: Gypsum

    Phosphates: Apatite

(C) Soil Forming Process

Pedogenic or Soil Forming Processes

    ☆ It is the geological weathering produces weathered rock material *i.e.* the parent material and when the genetic factors set the stage for soil development.

    ☆ The pedogenic processes change the parent material in to soil with varying horizonations.

    ☆ The pedogenic processes are extremely complex and dynamic involving many chemical and biological reactions, and usually operate simultaneously in a given area.

BASIC/FUNDAMENTAL PEDOGENIC PROCESSES

1) HUMIFICATION

A. Humification is the process of transformation (decomposition) of raw organic matter in to 'HUMUS'.

B. It is an extremely complex process involving various organisms such as bacteria, fungi, actinomycetes, earth worms and termites.

C. The decomposition of organic matter takes place in two phases: mineralization and humification. **Mineralization** is a biochemical breakdown of dead plant tissues by soil microorganisms to produce simple structured soluble organic substances, mineral compounds, metal cations and gases (CO_2). During the humification, soluble organic substances regroup themselves in to large molecules by polymerization and become poorly soluble. They form major part of soil humus and provide site for retention of cations. The other part of humus is the polysaccharides – gummy products of microbial excretions, which help in soil aggregation.

2) ELUVIATION

A. Eluviation means "Washing out". It is the process of removal of constituents in suspension or solution by the percolating water from the upper to lower layers.

B. The eluviation encompasses mobilization and translocation of mobile constituents resulting in textural differences.

3) ILLUVIATION

A. The process of deposition of soil materials (removed from the eluvial horizon "E") in the lower layer (or horizon of gains having the property of stabilizing translocated clay materials) is termed as "illuviation".

B. The horizons formed by this process are termed as illuvial horizons (B-horizon especially).

All these basic pedogenic processes, combine to result in a number of wide ranging soils that are observed on surface of the earth.

4) PODZOLIZATION

A. It is a process of soil formation resulting in the formation of podzols and podzolic soils.

B. It is the process of accumulation of silica and eluviation of sesquioxides.

5) LATERIZATION

A. In tropics, certain soils are massively impregnated with sesquioxides to the extent of 70 to 80 per cent of the total mass, and forms a cemented horizon, which when dried becomes very hard like a brick.

B. This soil forming process is called "laterization" or "lotozation" *e.g.* Soils of Malabar hills of Kerala.

6) GLEIZATION

A. The gleization is a process of soil formation resulting in the development of a glei (or gley) horizon in the lower part of the profile above the parent material due to poor drainage conditions or water logged conditions.

B. Such soils are called "hydromorphic soils". This process is not particularly dependant on climate (high rainfall as in humid regions) but often on drainage conditions.

7) SALINIZATION

A. It is the process of accumulation of salts such as sulphates, chlorides of calcium, magnesium, sodium and potassium in soils in the form of salty (salic) horizon.

B. The soils are called saline soils, which have ESP less than15 per cent and pH between 7 and 8.5.

C. Rainfall as in humid regions but often on drainage conditions.

8) SALONIZATION OR ALKALIZATION

A. The process involves the accumulation of sodium ions on the exchange complex of the clay to an extent of >15 per cent, resulting in the formation of sodic soils (solonetz) under arid and semi-arid conditions.

B. This occurs when anions like carbonates and bicarbonates predominate in soil.

9) SALODIZATION OR DEALKALIZATION

A. This process refers to the removal of Na^+ from exchange sites.

B. The Na^+ can be eliminated by increasing the concentration of Ca^{2+} or Mg^{2+} in the water, followed by improved drainage facilities.

(D) Classification of Soil

Different types of soil classification are:

(A) Physical classification: It is based on the physical properties like soil texture. The soils are termed as sandy, loamy, clay etc. Based on soil structure, soils are classified as single grained soils, aggregated soils etc.

(B) Chemical classification: It is based on the chemical properties of the soils. Calcareous soils, gypsiferous soils, alkaline soils, acidic soils etc.

(C) Geological classification: Two broad groups are recognized.

1. Residual/sedentary soils – soils developed in-situ from the underlying rocks.

2. Transported soils – soils developed from transported and deposited sediments.

(D) Physiographic classification: In this system, the characteristics of the landscape were considered. The soils are termed as levee soils, terrace soils, mountain soils, hilly soils, upland soils, lowland soils etc.

Other Types of Classifications

(A) Based on organic matter content: Organic soils and inorganic soils.

(B) Based on climate: Arid soils, humid soils, subhumid soils etc.

(C) Based on vegetation: Prairie soils, grassland soils, forest soils, etc.

SOILS OF INDIA

Indian Council of Agricultural Research (ICAR) has divided Indian soils into eight major groups:

1) Alluvial Soils

☆ Largest and the **most important soil group of India**.

☆ They are **composed of sediments deposited by rivers and the waves**.

☆ Their chemical composition makes them one of the most fertile in the world.

☆ They are mainly gray coloured.

☆ Usually deficient in nitrogen and humus (thus fertilizers are needed).

☆ Occupy the plains (from Punjab to Assam) and also occur in the valleys of Narmada and Tapti in M.P. and Gujarat, Mahanadi in the M.P. and Odisha, Godawari in A.P. and Cauvery in T.N.

☆ Can be divided into **Khadar** (new formed) and **Bhangar** (older, more clayey and kankary) alluvium.

2) Black Soils

☆ **Also called Regur and is ideal for cotton crop**.

☆ These soils have been formed due to the solidification of lava spread over large areas during volcanic activity in the Deccan Plateau, thousands of years ago.

☆ They are **black due to titaniferous magnetite**.

☆ Presence of montmorillonite clay (2:1).

☆ **Cracking problem** is most occurs.

☆ They have high moisture retention level, so best suitable for Dryland agriculture.

☆ Rich in Mn and Ca.

☆ **Deficient in N, P, Zn and organic matter**.

☆ Mainly found in Deccan Plateau - Maharashtra, Gujarat, M.P, Karnataka, Andhra Pradesh, Tamil Nadu.

☆ Apart from cotton cultivation, these fertile soils are suitable for growing cereals, oilseeds, citrus fruits and vegetables, tobacco and sugarcane.

3) Red Soils

☆ They are mainly formed due to the decomposition of ancient crystalline rocks like granites and gneisses and from rock types rich in minerals such as iron and magnesium.

☆ **The red colour of soil is due to the wide diffusion of iron oxides** through the materials of the soil.

☆ Covers almost the whole of Tamil Nadu, Karnataka, Andhra Pradesh, S.E. Maharashtra, Chhattisgarh, parts of Odisha, Jharkhand and Bundelkhand.

☆ Generally deficient in nitrogen, humus and phosphorus, but rich in potash.

☆ High phosphorus (P) fixation capacity due to pressure of kaolinite.

☆ Suitable for rice, millets, tobacco and vegetables (also groundnuts and potatoes at higher elevations).

4) Laterite Soils

☆ Found in typical monsoon conditions - under conditions of high temperature and heavy rainfall with alternate wet and dry periods.

☆ The alterations of wet and dry season leads to the leaching away of siliceous matter and lime of the rocks and a soil rich in oxides of iron and aluminium compounds is left behind.

☆ Found in parts of Western Ghats, Eastern Ghats, Rajmahal hills, Maharashtra, Karnataka, Kerala, Odisha, West Bengal, Assam, Tamil Nadu, etc.

☆ Poor in nitrogen and minerals.

☆ **Phosphorus fixation is most probable** in this soil.

☆ Best for tea, coffee, rubber, cinchona, coconut and suitable for rice and millet cultivation if manured.

5) Forest and Mountain Soils

☆ Such soils are mainly found on the hill slopes covered by forests.

☆ The formation of these soils is mainly governed by the characteristic deposition of organic matter derived from forest growth.

☆ In the Himalayan region, such soils are mainly found in valley basins, depressions and less steeply inclined slopes. Apart from the Himalayan region, the forest soils occur in higher hills in south and the peninsular region.

☆ They are generally brown coloured.

☆ Very rich in humus but are deficient in potash, phosphorus and lime and needs fertilizers.

☆ Plantation of tea, coffee, spices and tropical fruits.

6) Arid and Desert Soils

- ☆ A large part of the arid and semi-arid region in Rajasthan and adjoining areas of Punjab and Haryana lying between the Indus and the Aravallis receiving less than 50 cm of annual rainfall is affected by desert conditions.

- ☆ This area is covered by a mantle of sand which inhibits soil growth.

- ☆ The phosphate content of these soils is as high as in normal alluvial soils. Nitrogen is originally low but its deficiency is made up to some extent by the availability of nitrogen in the form of nitrates. Thus the presence of phosphates and nitrates make them fertile soils wherever moisture is available.

- ☆ The changes in the cropping pattern in the Indira Gandhi Canal Command Area are a living example of the utility of the desert soils.

7) Saline and Alkaline Soils

- ☆ In the drier parts of Bihar, U.P., Haryana, Punjab, Rajasthan and Maharashtra, are the salt-impregnated or alkaline soils. **Known by different names: Reh, kallar, USAR**, etc.

- ☆ Some of the salts are transported in solution by the rivers and canals, which percolates in the sub-soils of the plains.

- ☆ The accumulation of salts makes the soil infertile and renders it unfit for agriculture.

8) Peaty and Marshy Soils

- ☆ Peaty soils originate in the humid regions as a result of accumulation of large amounts of organic matter in the soil.

- ☆ They contain considerable amounts of soluble salts and 10 - 40 per cent of organic matter.

- ☆ **Peaty soils are** found in Kottayam and Alappuzha districts of Kerala, where it is called **Kari**.

- ☆ Peaty soils are generally Copper (Cu) deficient.

- ☆ Marshy soils, high in vegetable matter, are found in northern Bihar, coastal parts of Odisha, Tamil Nadu and West Bengal and parts of UP.

- ☆ Marshy soils are Zinc (Zn) deficient.

(E) Physical Properties of Soil

Different soil physical properties are:

1. Soil Structure

Arrangements of soil particles with crumbly and granular nature is considered good. Best size of soil aggregate for good growth of crop is (1-5mm) smaller aggregates may clog soil pores and larger ones may have large pore space.

Granular: Resembles cookie crumbs and is usually less than 0.5 cm in diameter. Commonly found in surface horizons where roots have been growing.	**Blocky**: Irregular blocks that are usually 1.5 - 5.0 cm in diameter.	**Prismatic**: Vertical columns of soil that might be a number of cm long. Usually found in lower horizons.
Columnar: Vertical columns of soil that have a salt "cap" at the top. Found in soils of arid climates.	**Platy**: Thin, flat plates of soil that lie horizontally. Usually found in compacted soil. Soil Science Society of America	**Single Grained**: Soil is broken into individual particles that do not stick together. Always accompanies a loose consistence. Commonly found in sandy soils.

Different Soil Structures

2. Soil Texture

☆ Relative proportion of different soil particles namely sand, silt and clay is known as soil texture.

☆ The principle textural classes are clay, clay loam, sandy clay, silt clay, sandy clay loam, silty clay loam, sandy loam, silt loam, sand, loamy sand and silt.

3. Soil Colour

☆ It is found out by using Munsell Colour Chart.

☆ Three variable are used to denote soil colour *i.e.* **Hue** – dominant wavelength, **Value** – relative lightness of the colour and **Chroma** - purity of the colour.

Classification of Soil Particles Based on Size (mm)

Classification		IISS	USDA
Stone	:	> 250	> 250
Cobble	:	75 - 250	75 - 250
Gravel	:	2 - 75	2 - 75
Very course sand	:	–	1.0 – 2.0
Course sand	:	2 - 0.2	0.5 – 1.0
Fine sand	:	0.2 -0.02	0.1 – 0.25
Very fine sand	:	–	0.05 – 0.1
Silt	:	0.02 – 0.002	0.002 – 0.05
Clay	:	< 0.002	< 0.002

4. Soil Plasticity and Cohesion

☆ Plasticity is the capacity of the soil to change its shape under moist conditions.

☆ Cohesion is the capacity to stick together.

☆ Plastic soils are cohesive.

5. Soil Colloids

☆ Soil colloid is made up of inorganic colloid (clay) and organic colloid (humus).

☆ Particles smaller than 1 micron are said to exhibit colloidal activity.

☆ Soil colloids have high exchange capacity, which increases with silica sesuioxides ratio.

6. Soil Water

☆ Water has maximum density at 4^{0}C. One molecule of water is attached to four molecules in the neighbourhood.

☆ The surface tension of water is 72.7 dyne/cm^2 at 25^{0}C.

☆ Structure of water molecules is hexagonal lattice and the angle is 104.5^0.

☆ Types of Soil water: Hygroscopic water, capillary water and gravitational water.

☆ **Hygroscopic water**: Water held at tension of more than 31-atm and not available to the plants.

☆ **Gravitational water**: Water held below 1/3rd-atm and drained from the soil due to gravity.

☆ **Wilting point**: Water held at tensions beyond 15-atm and is not available to the plants.

☆ **Field capacity**: If water is allowed to drain by gravity after supplying water, some water remains even after drainage due to gravity is called field capacity. Water at field capacity is held at $1/3^{rd}$ atm.

☆ **Available water**: Water held between $1/3^{rd}$ and 15 atm.

☆ Water in soil moves in response to difference to tension or pressure.

☆ Darcy's law in soil deals to hydraulic gradient.

7. Soil Air

☆ Soil air contains 10 times CO_2 concentration (0.3 per cent) as that of air.

☆ Ideally $2/3^{rd}$ of soil pores are filled with water and $1/3^{rd}$ with air.

☆ Fick's law deals about the diffusion of gases in soils.

☆ Soil air is characterised by ODR - Oxygen Diffusion Rate.

8. Soil Temperature

☆ In soil, heat is mainly transferred through **conduction**.

☆ Fourier's law deals with heat conduction in soils.

☆ Sandy soils absorb more heat than clays soils.

(F) Soil Organic Colloids

The **soil organic colloids** include highly decomposed organic matter generally called humus. Organic colloids are more reactive chemically and generally have a greater influence on soil properties per unit weight than the inorganic colloids. Humus is amorphous and its chemical and physical characteristics are not well defined. Clay minerals are usually crystalline (although some are amorphous) and usually have a characteristic chemical and physical configuration. Both inorganic and organic colloids are intimately mixed with other soil solids. Thus, the bulk of the soil solids are essentially inert and the majority of the soil's physical and chemical character is a result of the colloids present.

Soil Organic Colloids may helps:

1. To determine the organic matter content of soil.
2. To determine the contribution of organic colloids to soil cation exchange capacity.
3. To understand the pH-dependency of charge on organic colloids.

(G) Soil Organic Matters

Soil organic matter: Any material of plant or animal origin found in the soil is known as Organic matter.

Organic matter that is well decomposed and digested by many kinds of soil micro organisms and converted into fairly stable, amorphous, brown to black material is termed as **"Humus"**. It is very difficult to identify the parent material from which it is derived.

Uses of Organic Matter

1. Helps in aggregation of soil particles and improves the structure, permeability and WHC and aeration,

2. It serves as a reservoir of plant nutrients,

3. Organic acids and CO_2 produced during decomposition help to dissolve minerals like 'P', 'K' and make them more available,

4. It helps in maintaining soil pH,

5. Leaching of certain cations like K, Ca, Mg, NH_4 is prevented because of its higher CEC,

6. It is the source of energy for micro organisms, earthworms and other living things,

7. Helps to maintain soil temperature, and

8. Alkalinity is reduced.

Organic matter also stabilizes soil aggregates, provides a storehouse for many important plant nutrients, and provides an energy source and habitat for abundant soil microorganisms. Mineral soils typically contain about **1-5 per cent organic matter**, but practically all soil physical and chemical processes are strongly impacted by its presence. Organic soils, which are common in wet environments, contain more organic material–generally greater that 20 per cent, depending on clay content.

Organic matter originates from the decomposition of the tissues of plants, animals, and microorganisms. The most chemically and physically active form of SOM is a dark, amorphous material collectively called **humus**. Unlike much of the soil organic fraction, which is in a constant state of flux, humus is relatively stable. It and other organic components can, and are, however, broken down slowly, providing an abundant energy source for soil microorganisms. The process is essentially oxidative. We will accelerate this process in the lab by combusting soils to determine their organic matter content as well as some of the soil properties imparted by SOM.

(H) Irrigation Water Quality

☆ Water, either from precipitation or ground, never remains pure as the movement it is converted into liquid form from vapour it gets mixed with atmospheric gases and after reaching on the earth it is mixed with various salts, minerals and even heavy metals.

☆ The prime contaminations of irrigation water are irons like sodium, calcium, magnesium and potassium while anions are like carbonate bicarbonate, chloride, sulphate and nitrate.

☆ The quality of irrigation water is mostly expressed on the basis of total salt concentration in water, relative Na concentration to other cations, bicarbonate content and boron concentration.

Evaluation of Salt Content in Irrigation Water (USSAR)

Salt Content (g l⁻¹)		Evaluation
0.2 to 0.5	:	Water of the best quality
1 to 2	:	Water causing salinity and alkalinity hazard
3 to 7	:	Leaching and perfect drainage

US Soil Salinity Laboratory's Grouping of Irrigation Water

Classification of Water			EC (m.mhos/cm)	Salt Concentration (g/lt)	Remarks
C₁	Low salinity water	:	0–250	Less than 0.16	Safe
C₂	Medium salinity water	:	250–750	0.16–0.5	Needs leaching
C₃	High salinity water	:	750–2250	0.5–1.5	Not suitable
C₄	Very high salinity water		2250–5000	1.5–3.0	Not suitable

Bicarbonate Content of Irrigation Water

☆ Carbonate associates quickly with Ca and Mg and form $CaCO_3$ and $MgCO_3$. The Na replaces Ca and Mg and synthesises Na_2CO_3 which again causes sodium hazard (called as Residual Sodium Carbonate. RSC)

RSC in Water (m.eq/l)		Suitability for Irrigation	Remarks
> 2.5	:	Not suitable for irrigation	Needs gypsum
1.25 – 2.5	:	Marginal	Needs gypsum
Less than 1.25	:	Safe	—

Sodium Hazard of Irrigation Water

$$SAR = \frac{Na}{\sqrt{[Ca + Mg / 2]}}$$

Sodium Hazard		Class	SAR
Low	:	S₁	<10
Medium	:	S₂	10 - 18
High	:	S₃	18 - 26
Very high		S₄	26 - 31

Boron Hazard of Irrigation Water

Class		Boron (ppm)	Suitability
Normal water	C_1 :	<3	Ideal for all crops on all soils
Low boron water	C_2 :	3–4	All crops on heavy and medium soils
Medium boron water	C_3 :	4–5	Can be used for most crops on heavy soils
Boron water	C_4 :	5–10	Semi-tolerate and tolerate crops on heavy soils
High boron water	C_5 :	>10	Not suitable for irrigation

Relationship between EC, SAR and RSC (meq l^{-1})

	Rating		$EC x 10^3$	SAR	RSC
A	Good	:	< 2	< 10	< 2.5
B	Normal	:	2 - 4	< 10	< 2.5
C	Sodic	:	< 4.0	> 10	> 2.5
D	Marginally saline	:	4 - 8	< 10	0.0
E	Poor	:	> 8.0	< 10	> 2.5

(I) Soil Reaction

There are three major reactions found in soils:

1. Acidic reaction - formation of Acidic Soils
2. Alkaline reaction - formation of Alkaline Soils
3. Saline reaction - formation of Saline Soils

1) Acid Soils

The soils with pH less than 6.5 and which respond to liming may be considered as acidic soils.

a) Reasons for Acidity

☆ Humus decomposition results in release of large amounts of acids. There by lowering the pH.

☆ Rainfall: In areas with more than 100 cm rainfall associated with high R.H., Ca, Mg is dissolved in water and leached out due to this base saturation of soil decreases.

☆ Application of elemental sulphur under goes reactions resulting in formation of H_2SO_4.

☆ Continuous application of acid forming fertilizers like ammonium sulphates or ammonium chlorides results in depletion of Ca by CEC (cation exchange capacity) phenomenon.

☆ Parent Material: Generally rocks are considered as acidic, which contain large amount of silica (SiO_2) when this combined with water, acidity increases.

b) Characteristics

☆ pH is less than 6.5.

☆ These soils are open textured with high massive Structure.

☆ Low in Ca, Mg with negligible amount of soluble salts.

☆ These soils appear as brown or reddish brown, sandy loams or sands.

c) Injury to Crops

i) Direct Affects

☆ Plant root system does not grow normally due to toxic hydrogen ions.

☆ Permeability of plant membranes are adversely affected due to soil acidity.

☆ Enzyme actions may be altered, since they are sensitive to pH changes.

ii) Indirect Affects

☆ Deficiency of Ca and Mg occur by leaching.

☆ Al, Mn and Fe available in toxic amounts.

☆ All the micro nutrients except molybdenum are available. So 'Mo' deficiency has been identified in leguminous crops.

☆ Phosphorous gets immobilized and its availability is reduced.

iii) Effect on Activity of Microorganisms

☆ Most of the activities of beneficial organisms like Azatobactor and nodule forming bacteria of legumes are adversely affected as acidity increases.

d) Crops Suitable for Cultivation in Acidic Soils

pH Level		Acidic Soils
4.5	:	Citrus, Blue berries
5.0	:	Tobacco, Apple, Grapes, Plum, Watermelon
5.5	:	Cowpea, Soybean, Cotton, Wheat, Oat, Peas, Tomato, Sorghum
6.0	:	Peanut, Cabbage, Carrot, Onion, Radish, Spinach, Cauliflower
6.5	:	Alfalfa, Sugarbeet

e) Amelioration

★ Lime as reclaiming agent: Lime is added to neutralize acidity and to increase the pH, so that the availability of nutrients will be increased.

★ Basic slag obtained from Iron and steel industry can be substituted for lime. It contains about 48-54 per cent of CaO and 3-4 per cent MgO.

★ Ammonium sulphate and Ammonium chloride should not be applied to acid soils but urea can be applied.

★ Calcium Ammonium Nitrate (CAN) is suitable to acidic soils.

★ Any citrate soluble phosphate fertilizer is good source of phosphorus for acidic soils.

★ *e.g.* Dicalcium phosphate (DCP), Tricalcium phosphate (TCP)

Potassium sulphate is a suitable source of 'K' for acidic soils. But MOP is better than K_2SO_4 because Cl⁻ of MOP replaces -OH ions, their by release of -OH ions tends to increase the pH.

2) Alkaline Soils

Alkali soils are formed due to concentration of exchangeable sodium and high pH. Because of high alkalinity resulting from sodium carbonate the surface soil is discoloured to black; hence the term black alkali is used.

a) Reasons for Alkalinity

★ The excessive irrigation of uplands containing Na salts results in the accumulation of salts in the valleys.

★ In arid and semi arid areas salt formed during weathering are not fully leached.

★ In coastal areas if the soil contains carbonates the ingression of sea water leads to the formation of alkali soils due to formation of sodium carbonates.

★ Irrigated soils with poor drainage.

b) Characteristics

★ Saline soil have soil pH of more than 8.5

★ Ec is less than 4.0 m.mhos/cm

★ ESP (exchangeable sodium per cent) is more than 15

★ It has black colour that why it is also called as *Black alkali*

c) Injury to Crops

★ High exchangeable sodium decreases the availability of calcium, magnesium to plants.

★ Dispersion of soil particles due to high exchangeable 'Na' leads to poor physical condition of soil, low permeability to water and air, tends to be sticky when wet and becomes hard on drying.

☆ Toxicity due to excess hydroxyl and carbonate ions.

☆ Growth of plant gets affected mainly due to nutritional imbalance.

☆ Restricted root system and delay in flowering in sensitive varieties.

☆ Typical leaf burn in annuals and woody plants due to excess of chloride and sodium.

☆ Bronzing of leaves in citrus.

☆ It effects the solubility of zinc (Zn).

d) Crops Suitable for Cultivation in Alkaline Soils

☆ Barley, Sugarbeet, Cotton, Sugarcane, Mustard, Rice, Maize, Red gram, Greengram, Sunflower, Linseed, Sesame, Bajra, Sorghum, Tomato, Cabbage, Cauliflower, Cucumber, Pumpkin, Bittergaurd. Beetroot, Guava, Asparagus, Banana, Spinach, Coconut, Grape, Datepalm, Pomegranate.

e) Amelioration

☆ The process of amelioration consists of two steps:

❖ To convert exchangeable sodium into water soluble form.

❖ To leach out the soluble sodium from the field. Amendments used for reclamation of Alkali soils.

❖ **Gypsum -** For every 1 m.e. of exchangeable Na per 100 g of soil, 1.7 tones of Gypsum/acre is to be added.

Application

☆ If the requirement is 3 tonnes/acre- apply in one dose.

☆ If the requirement is 3 to 5 tonnes/acre- apply in 2 split doses.

☆ If the requirement is 5 or more tonnes/acre - apply in 3 split doses.

☆ Use of Pyrites (FeS_2). Sulphur present in pyrites causes decrease in pH of soil due to formation of H_2SO_4.

☆ Application of sulphur.

☆ Application of molasses.

☆ Drainage channels must be arranged around the field.

☆ Growing of green manuring crops and incorporate them in the field.

3) Saline Soils

The saline soils contain toxic concentration of soluble salts in the root zone. Soluble salts consist of chlorides and sulphates of sodium, calcium, magnesium. Because of the white encrustation formed due to salts, the saline soils are also called white alkali soils.

a) Reasons for Salinity

☆ In arid and semi arid areas, salts formed during weathering are not fully leached. During the periods of higher rainfall the soluble salts are leached from the more permeable high laying areas to low laying areas and where ever the drainage is restricted, salts accumulate on the soil surface, as water evaporates

☆ The excessive irrigation of uplands containing salts results in the accumulation of salts in the valleys.

☆ In areas having salt layer at lower depths in the profile, seasonal irrigation may favour the upward movement of salts.

☆ Salinity is also caused if the soils are irrigated with saline water.

☆ In coastal areas the ingress of sea water induces salinity in the soil.

b) Characteristics

☆ Saline soil have soil pH of less than 8.5

☆ EC is more than 4.0 m.mhos/cm

☆ ESP (exchangeable sodium per cent) is less than 15

☆ Dominated by sulphate and chloride ions and low in exchangeable sodium

☆ Flocculation due to excess soluble salts.

☆ High osmotic pressure of soil solution

☆ Presence of white crust

☆ It has white colour that why it is also called as *White alkali*

c) Injury to Crops

☆ High osmotic pressure decreases the water availability to plants hence retardation of growth rate.

☆ As a result of retarded growth rate, leaves and stems of affected plants are stunted.

☆ Development of thicker layer of surface wax imparts bluish green tinge on leaves.

☆ Due to high EC germination per cent of seeds is reduced.

d) Crops Suitable For Cultivation in Saline Soils

☆ Barley, Sugarbeet, Cotton, Sugarcane, Mustard, Rice, Maize, Red gram, Greengram, Sunflower, Linseed, Sesame, Bajra, Sorghum, Tomato, Cabbage, Cauliflower, Cucumber, Pumpkin, Bitterguard. Beetroot, Guava, Asparagus, Banana, Spinach, Coconut, Grape, Datepalm, Pomegranate.

e) Amelioration

☆ The salts are to be leached below the root zone and not allowed to come up. However this practice is some what difficult in deep and fine textured soils containing more salts in the lower layers. Under these conditions, a provision of some kind of sub-surface drains becomes important.

☆ The required area is to be made into smaller plots and each plot should be bounded to hold irrigation water.

☆ Separate irrigation and drainage channels are to be provided for each plot.

☆ Plots are to be flooded with good quality water upto 15 - 20 cm and puddled. Thus, soluble salts will be dissolved in the water. The excess water with dissolved salts is to be removed into the drainage channels.

☆ Flooding and drainage are to be repeated 5 or 6 times, till the soluble salts are leached from the soil to a safer limit.

☆ Green manure crops like Daincha can be grown up to flowering stage and incorporated into the soil. Paddy straw can also be used.

☆ Super phosphate, Ammonium sulphate or Urea can be applied in the last puddle. MOP and Ammonium chlorides should not be used.

☆ Scrape the salt layer on the surface of the soil with spade.

☆ Grow salt tolerant crops like sugar beet, tomato, beet root, barley etc.

Before sowing, the seeds are to be treated by soaking the seeds in 0.1 per cent salt solution for 2 to 3   hours.

(J) Essential Plant Nutrients

Plant contains more than 90 elements, out of which, 17 elements are known to be essential which are classified as macr-onutrients and micro-nutrients, based on their relative abundance in plants.

Essentials nutrients	-	C, H, O, N, P, K, Ca, Mg, S, Fe, Mn, Mo, Cu, Cl, B, Zn, Ni = **17** * Nickel (Ni) is the latest (1987) addition to the list of essential nutrients
Primary nutrients	-	N, P and K = 3
Secondary nutrients	-	Ca, Mg and S = 3
Macro-nutrients	-	N, P, K, Ca, Mg and S = 6
Micro-nutrients	-	Fe, Mn, Mo, Cu, Cl, Co, B, Zn = 8
Functional nutrients	-	Essential elements + Co, V, Si, Na = 21

ESSENTIALITY OF ELEMENTS IN PLANT NUTRITION

Arnon and Stout (1939) and Arnon (1952) proposed the following criteria of essentiality of mineral nutrients:

1) A deficiency of the element in question results in failure to complete the life cycle,

2) Deficiency of element in question can be corrected only by supplying that particular element, and

3) The element must extend its effect directly on growth or metabolism and not by indirect effect such as antagonism of another element present at a toxic level.

Essential Nutrients for Plant Growth and their Principal Forms for Uptake

Nutrient	Chemical Symbol	Principal forms for uptake
Carbon	C	CO_2
Hydrogen	H	H_2O, H^+
Oxygen	O	H_2O, O^{2+}
Nitrogen	N	NH_4^+, NO_3^-
Phosphorus	P	$H_2PO_4^-, HPO_4^{2-}, PO_4^{3-}$
Potassium	K	K^+
Calcium	Ca	Ca^{2+}
Magnesium	Mg	Mg^{2+}
Sulphur	S	SO_4^{2-}, SO_2
Iron	Fe	Fe^{2+}, Fe^{3+}
Manganese	Mn	Mn^{2+}
Boron	B	$H_2BO_3^-, B_4O_7^{2-}, BO_3^{3-}$
Zinc	Zn	Zn^{2+}
Copper	Cu	Cu^{2+}
Molybdenum	Mo	MoO_4^{2-}
Chlorine	Cl	Cl^-

Functions of Essential Nutrients in Plants

Nutrient	Functions
Carbon	Basic molecular component of carbohydrates, proteins, lipids, and nucleic acids.
Oxygen	Oxygen is somewhat like carbon in that it occurs in virtually all organic compounds of living organisms.
Hydrogen	Hydrogen plays a central role in plant metabolism. Important in ionic balance and as main reducing agent and plays a key role in energy relations of cells.
Nitrogen	Nitrogen is a component of many important organic compounds ranging from proteins to nucleic acids.

Nutrient	Functions
Phosphorus	Central role in plants is in energy transfer and protein metabolism.
Potassium	Helps in osmotic and ionic regulation. Potassium functions as a cofactor or activator for many enzymes of carbohydrate and protein metabolism.
Calcium	Calcium is involved in cell division and plays a major role in the maintenance of membrane integrity.
Magnesium	Component of chlorophyll and a cofactor for many enzymatic reactions.
Sulphur	Sulphur is somewhat like phosphorus in that it is involved in plant cell energetic.
Iron	An essential component of many heme and nonheme Fe enzymes and carries, including the Cytochormes (respiratory electron carriers) and the ferredoxins. The latter are involved in key metabolic function such as N fixation, photosynthesis, and electron transfer.
Zinc	Essential component of several dehydrogenases, and peptidases, including carbonic anhydrase, alcohol dehydrogenase, glutamic dehydrogenase, and malic dehdyrogenase, among others.
Manganese	Involved in the O_2 – evolving system of photosynthesis and is a component of the enzymes arginase and phospho transferases.
Copper	Constituent of a number of important enzymes, including cytochrome oxidize, ascorbic acid oxidase, and laccase.
Boron	Involved in carbohydrate metabolism and synthesis of cell wall components.
Molybdenum	Required for the normal assimilation of N in plants. An essential component of nitrate reductase as well as nitrogenase (N_2 fixation enzyme).
Chlorine	Essential for photosynthesis and as an activator of enzymes involved in splitting water. It also functions in osmo-regulation of plants growing on saline soils.

NUTRIENT DEFICIENCY SYMPTOMS OF PLANTS

Nutrient deficiency symptoms may be classified as follows:

1. Complete crop failure at the seedling stage.
2. Severe stunting of plants.
3. Specific leaf symptoms appearing at varying times during the season.
4. Internal abnormalities such as clogged conductive tissues.
5. Delayed or abnormal maturity.

6. Obvious yield differences, with or without leaf symptoms.

7. Poor quality of crops, including differences in protein, oil, or starch content, and storage quality.

8. Yield differences detected only by careful experimental work.

Appearance of Deficiency Symptoms

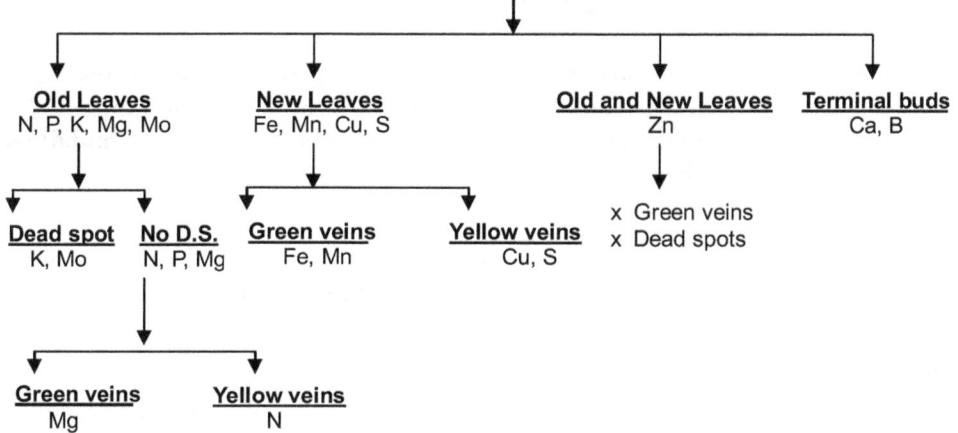

Old Leaves N, P, K, Mg, Mo	**New Leaves** Fe, Mn, Cu, S	**Old and New Leaves** Zn	**Terminal buds** Ca, B

Dead spot K, Mo	**No D.S.** N, P, Mg	**Green veins** Fe, Mn	**Yellow veins** Cu, S	x Green veins x Dead spots

Green veins Mg	**Yellow veins** N

Generalized Visual Symptoms of Nutrient Deficiency on Plant

Element/Status	*Visual Symptoms*
Nitrogen (N)	
Deficiency	Uniform yellowing of older leaves including veins, leaves that will eventually turn brown and die. Plant growth is slow; plants will be stunted, and will mature early, Cereal crops show 'V' shaped pale yellowing at lower leaf tips. Deficiency causes **'Buttoning in Cauliflower'**.
Phosphorus (P)	
Deficiency	Plant growth will be slow and stunted, and the older leaves will have a purple coloration, particularly on the underside, rear sides develop bronzy appearance, premature leaf falling is most common. Deficiency causes **'Sickle leaf disease'**
Potassium (K)	
Deficiency	Yellowing starts from tip/margin of lower leaves and extend to center of leaf base. Yellowing parts become dead spots (necrotic). The edges of older leaves will look burned, a symptom known as *scorch*. **Scorching and burning on margins of bottom leaves are most common.**

Element/Status	*Visual Symptoms*
Calcium (Ca)	
Deficiency	Terminal bud leaf become chlorotic white with base remain green. 1/3 chlorotic portion of tip hooks downward and brittle. Death of terminal buds. Deficiency causes **'Blossom end rot' in Tomato and Ber** and **'Tip hooking in Cauliflower'**
Magnesium (Mg)	
Deficiency	Older leaves will be yellow between veins and veins remain green (**Interveinal chlorosis**). Leaves become mottled. Also affects chlorophyll formation. Deficiency causes **'Sand drawn disease' in tobacco**.
Sulfur (S)	
Deficiency	Yellowing of leaves. Leaves are paler than interveinal portion. Occurrence of **'downward cupping of leaves' in Tobacco and Tea**.
Boron (B)	
Deficiency	Yellowing/chlorosis starts from base of terminal bud leaf and extends to tip results in appearance of **'Whip like structure'** and become brownish/blackish brown. Deficiency causes **'Internal necrosis in Aonla and Mango'**, **'Hen and Chicken disorder in Grape'** and **'Heart rot in Sugarbeet'**.
Chlorine (Cl)	
Deficiency	**Younger leaves will be chlorotic and plants will easily wilt. For wheat, a plant disease will infest the plant when Cl is deficient.**
Copper (Cu)	
Deficiency	Leaves including veins become yellow and tending towards whiteness. Occurrence of **'Marginal leaf burning'**. Deficiency causes **'Dia back and Little leaf disease in Citrus '**.
Iron (Fe)	
Deficiency	Veins remain conspicuously green and other leaf portion turn yellow and tending towards whiteness. **Interveinal chlorosis will occur**. Deficiency causes **'Leaf bleaching in sugarcane** and **'Ivory white of Paddy'**.
Manganese (Mn)	
Deficiency	Interveinal yellowing of young leaves but not tending towards whiteness. Veins remain green. Deficiency causes **'Marsh disease in Pea'**

Element/Status	Visual Symptoms
Molybdenum (Mo)	
Deficiency	Older and middle leaves become chlorotic first. Translucent spots of irregular shape between veins; spots become impregnated with resinous gum. Occurrence of '**Typical Interveinal chlorosis**'. Deficiency causes '**Whiptail disease and Browning in Cauliflower**'.
Zinc (Zn)	
Deficiency	Upper leaves will show chlorosis on midrib. Veins green and dead spots occur in all parts of leaf (veins, tips and margins). Plants appear bushy due to reduced internodal elongation. '**White bud of Maize**' is caused by the deficiency.

(K) Inorganic Fertilizers

Fertilizers

Fertilizers are the inorganic materials which are added to the soil to supply certain elements essential to the growth of plants.

Classification of Fertilizers

1. *Straight fertilizers*: Fertilizers which contain only one primary or major nutrient, *e.g.* Urea.

2. *Binary fertilizers*: Fertilizers which contain two major nutrients *e.g.* Potassium nitrate.

3. *Ternary fertilizers*: Fertilizers which contain three major nutrients *e.g.* Ammonium potassium phosphate.

4. *Complete fertilizers*: Those fertilizers having all the three major nutrients *viz.* N, P and K.

5. *Complex fertilizers*: Such fertilizers contain more than one primary or major nutrient element *e.g.* DAP, Ammonium phosphate.

Average Nutrient Content of Common Fertilizers

Fertilizers	Nutrient Content (per cent)			
	N	P_2O_5	K_2O	Remark
Nitrogenous Fertilizers				
(A) Nitrate form:				
1. Sodium nitrate	16.0	-	-	
2. Calcium nitrate	15.5	-	-	

Fertilizers	Nutrient Content (per cent)			
	N	P_2O_5	K_2O	Remark
(B) Ammonical form:				
1. Ammonium phosphate	16.0	20.0	-	
2. Ammonium chloride	24-26	-	-	Used for coconut, oil palm
3. Ammonium sulphate	21.0	-	-	Oldest N-fertilizer, Best for top dressing in rice
4. Anhydrous ammonia	81.0	-	-	
(C) Ammonical Nitrate form:				
1. Ammonium nitrate	33-34	-	-	Fire hazardous fertilizer
2. Calcium ammonium nitrate	26.0	-	-	Nitro chalk/lime, Kisan khad, Neutral fertilizer
3. Ammonium sulphate nitrate	26.0	-	-	
(D) Amide form:				
1. Urea	46.0	-	-	Only organic N-fertilizer, cheapest and suitable for foliar spray
2. Calcium cynide	21.0	-	-	
Phosphatic Fertilizers				
(A) Water soluble:				
1. Superphosphate (single)	-	16-18	-	Oldest commercially available fertilizer
2. Superphosphate (double)	-	32.0	-	
3. Superphosphate (triple)	-	46-48	-	
(B) Citric acid soluble:				
1. Dicalcium phosphate	-	34-39	-	
2. Basic slag	-	14-18	-	
3. Bone meal	-	23-30	-	Suitable for acidic and long duration crops
(C) Insoluble:				
1. Rock phosphate	-	20-40	-	
2. Rock bone meal	-	20-25	-	
3. Steamed bone meal	-	22.0	-	

Fertilizers	Nutrient Content (per cent)			
	N	P_2O_5	K_2O	Remark
Potassic Fertilizers				
1. Muriate of potash/KCl	-	60.0	-	
2. Sulphate of potash	-	48.0	-	
3. Potassium nitrate	-	44.0	-	Suitable for fertigation, also k/s Salt petre or Nitre

(L) Methods of Fertilizer Application to Crops

FOR SOLID FERTILIZERS

1. **Broadcasting:** Broadcasting is the method of application of fertilizer uniformly over the entire field. It may be at planting or in standing crop as top dressing. This method is adopted under certain conditions.

2. **Top dressing:** Top dressing is application of fertilizer to the standing crop, especially nitrate nitrogenous fertilizers.

3. **Placement:** Inserting or drilling or placing the fertilizer below the soil surface by means of any tool or implement at desired depth to supply plant nutrients to crop either before sowing or in the standing crop is called placement. With placement methods, fertilizers are placed in the soil irrespective of the position of seed, seedling or growing plants before sowing or after sowing the crops. The following methods are most common in this category:

   A. **Plough - sole Placement:** The fertilizer is placed in a continuous band on the bottom of the furrow during the process of ploughing. Each band is covered as the next furrow is turned. By this method, fertilizer is placed in moist soil where it can become more available to growing plants during dry seasons.

   B. **Deep Placement:** In this method, ammonical nitrogenous fertilizer like ammonium sulphate or ammonium forming nitrogenous fertilizer like urea is placed in the reduced zone to avoid nitrogen loss in lowland rice and is available to the crop during the active vegetative period.

   C. **Sub - Soil Placement:** This refers to the placement of fertilizers in the sub-soil with the help of heavy power machinery. This method is recommended in humid and sub-humid regions where many sub-soils are strongly acidic. Due to acidic conditions the level of available plant nutrients is extremely low. Under these conditions, fertilizers, especially phosphatic and potassic are placed in the sub-soil for better root development.

   D. **Localized Placement:** This method refers to the application of fertilizers into the soil close to the seed or plant. Localised placement is usually employed when relatively small quantities of fertilizers are to be applied. Localised placement reduces fixation of phosphorus and potassium.

E. **Bulk blending:** It is the process of mixing two or more different fertilizers varying in physical and chemical composition without any adverse effects. For this formulation certain additional materials called 'Fillers' and 'Conditioners' are used to improve the physical condition of the mixed fertilizer. This mixed fertilizer should be applied as top dressing.

F. **Contact or drill placement:** It refers to drilling seed and fertilizer simultaneously at sowing. Ferti seed drills are popular in Dryland agriculture for drill placement.

G. **Band placement:** It consists of applying the fertilizer in continuous or discontinuous bands close to the one   or both sides of seed or plant. This method is well suited for wider spaced crops *i.e.* sugarcane, tobacco, cotton, castor, maize and vegetables.

H. **Pellet placement:** Application of fertilizer, especially nitrogen in pellet form to the lowland rice to avoid nitrogen loss. Soil and fertilizer are mixed in the ratio of 1;10 or 15 in the form of small pellets and placed in the reduced zone.

FOR LIQUID FERTILIZATION

The use of liquid fertilizers as a means of fertilization has assumed considerable importance in foreign countries.

1. **Starter solution:** Solutions of fertilizers, generally prepared in low concentration.

   ☆ It consists of N_2, P_2O_5, and K_2O in the ratio of 1:2:1 and 1:1:2 are applied for soaking seed, dipping roots or spraying on seedlings for early establishment and growth.

   ☆ The nutrients reach the plant roots immediately.

   ☆ The solution is sufficiently diluted so that it does not inhibit growth.

   ☆ This method is specially applied in pulses and vegetable crops.

2. **Foliar spray:** In this method, nutrients are applied to the standing crops in the form of spray for quick recovery from the deficiency. It avoids fixation of nutrients in the soil.

3. **Soil application:** Direct application of liquid fertilizers to the soil need special injecting equipment. Anhydrous ammonia (a liquid under high pressure up to 14 kg per square cm or more) and nitrogen solutions are directly applied to the soil. Liquid manures such as urine, sewage water and shed washing are directly let into the field.

4. **Fertigation:** Fertigation is the application of fertilizer with irrigation water in either open or closed system. The open system includes lined and unlined open ditches and gated pipes that are used for furrow and flood irrigation.

Sprinkler and drip systems are the main closed systems. Nitrogen and sulphur are the principal nutrients applied by Fertigation. This saves the application cost and allows the utilization of relatively in expensive water-soluble fertilizers.

Chapter 2
Agronomy

(A) Definition and Scope of Agronomy

☆ **The term** "Agronomy" **is derived from Greek word** 'Agros' **means** 'Field' **and** 'Nomos' **means** 'to manage'.

Definition of Agronomy

1. "Agronomy is a branch of agricultural science which deals with principles and practices of soil, water and crop management".

2. It is branch of agril science that deals with methods which provide favourable environment to the crop for higher productively,

Scope of Agronomy (Agriculture)

Agronomy is a dynamic discipline of agriculture deals with the proper management of soil, crop and water. It plays a greater role in agriculture for crop production to fulfill the increasing demand of human population. Proverbially, India is known as "Land of Villages". Near about 67 per cent of India's population live in villages. The occupation of villagers is crop production (agriculture). Agriculture is the dominant sector of our economy and contributes in various ways such as:

☆ **National Economy:** In 2009-10, agriculture contributed 14.6 per cent of the National Income of India, in which crop production plays a major role.

☆ **Total Employment:** Around 65 per cent population is working and depends on agriculture and allied activities. Nearly 70 per cent of the rural population earns its livelihood from agriculture and other occupation allied to agriculture. In cities also, a considerable part of labour force is engaged in jobs depending on processing and marketing of agricultural products.

☆ **Industrial Inputs:** Most of the industries depend on the raw material produced by agriculture, so agriculture is the principal source of raw material to the industries. The industries like cotton textile, jute, paper, sugar depends totally on agriculture for the supply of raw material. The small scale and cottage industries like handloom and power loon, ginning and pressing, oil crushing, rice husking, sericulture fruit processing, etc are also mainly agro based industries.

☆ **Food Supply:** During 2010-11, estimated food grains production was 218.20 million tons and which is to be increased about 240 million tons by the end of this century to feed the growing population of India *i.e.* 35 crores in 1951 and 100 crores at the end of this century. India, thus, is able to meet almost all the need of its population with regards to food by develop intensive program for increasing food production.

☆ **State Revenue:** The agriculture is contributing the revenue by agriculture taxation includes direct tax and indirect tax. Direct tax includes land revenue, cesses and surcharge on land revenue, cesses on crops and agril income tax. Indirect tax induces sales tax, custom duty and local taxes etc. which farmer pay on purchase of agriculture inputs.

☆ **Trade:** Agriculture plays and important role in foreign trade attracting valuable foreign exchange, necessary for our economic development. The product from agriculture based industries such as jute, cloth, tinned food, etc. contributed to 10.23 per cent of our national export. Around 50 per cent of total exports are contributed by agril sector. Indian agriculture plays and important role in roads, rails and waterways outside the countries. Indian in roads, rails and waterways used to transport considerable amount of agril produce and agro based industrial products. Agril products like tea, coffee, sugar, oil seeds, tobacco; spices, etc. also constitute the main items of export from India.

(B) Classification of Crops

A) Classification based on Season

1. Kharif Crops

The Kharif/monsoon crop is sown with the beginning of the first rains in June to July, during the south-west monsoon season and harvest in the month of October. Require warm, wet weather at major period of crop growth, also required short day length for flowering. The term Kharif means "autumn" in Arabic. *e.g.* Paddy, Maize, Soybean, Sorghum, Groundnut, Cotton, Urd etc.

2. Rabi Crops

The Rabi/winter crop or spring harvest crop is sown in the month of November during the north-east monsoon season and harvest in the month of February. Crops grow well in cold and dry weather. Require longer day length for flowering. The term Rabi means "spring" in Arabic. *e.g.* Wheat, Chickpea, Pea, Sunflower, Safflower, Mustard etc.

3. Zaid Crops

The Zaid/summer crop is mainly sown in the month of March and harvested in May. Require warm day weather for major growth period and longer day length for flowering. *e.g.* Paddy, Groundnut, Moong, Sunflower, Maize, Groundnuts, Watermelon, Pumpkins, Gourds.

B) Classification Based on Taxonomy

	Family		Crops
1.	Asteraceae/Compositae	:	Sunflower, Safflower, Niger
2.	Cruciferae	:	Mustard, Radish, Cabbage, Cauliflower etc
3.	Cucurbitaceae	:	Bottlegaurd, Bittergaurd, Pumpkin etc.
4.	Chenopodiaceae	:	Sugarbeet, Beet, Spinach
5.	Euphorbiaceae	:	Castor, Topioca
6.	Malvaceae	:	Cotton, Ladyfinger, Rosette
7.	Papilionaceae/ Leguminoceae	:	Pea, Gram, Arhar, Groundnut, Berseem, Lathyrus, Sunhemp, Lucerne, Urd, Moong, Lentil etc.
8.	Pedaliaceae	:	Sesamum (Til)
9.	Poaceae/Graminae	:	Cereals, Millets. Grasses, Sugarcane, Napier, Oat
10.	Polygonaceae	:	Buckwheat
11.	Solanaceae	:	Potato, Tobacco, Tomato, Chilli, Brinjal

C) Classification Based on Botany

Crops		Botanical Name
Cereal Crops		
Rice	:	*Oryza sativa* L.
Wheat	:	*Triticum aestivum* L.
Maize	:	*Zea mays* L.
Bajra/Pearlmillet	:	*Pennisetum typhoides/P. glaucum* L.
Sorghum/Jowar	:	*Sorghum bicolor/S. vulgare* L. Moench
Barley	:	*Hordeum vulgare* L.
Triticale	:	*Secale cereal*
Buckwheat/Pseudo cereal	:	*Fagopyrum esculentum*

Crops	Botanical Name
Millet Crops	
Cheena/Proso millet	: *Panicum miliacearum*
Foxtail/Italian/ Jerman millet/Kakun	: *Seteria italica* L. Beauv.
Kodo/Coarsest millet	: *Paspulum scrobiculatum* L.
Little millet	: *Panicum sumatrense*
Madua/Ragi/Finger millet	: *Eleusine coracana* Gaertn
Sawan/Barnyard millet	: *Echinochloa frumentance* L.
Pulse Crops	
Gram/Chickpea/Bengal gram	: *Cicer aeritinum* L.
Field Pea/Grain pea	: *Pisum sativum var. arvense*
Arhar/Pigeon pea/ Red gram	: *Cajanus cajan* L. Millsp.
Soybean	: *Glycine max* L. Merril
Black gram/Urdbean	: *Vigna mungo/Phaseolus mungo* L. Hepper
Green gram/Moong/ Moongbean	: *Vigna radiate/Phaseolus aureus* L. Wilczek
French bean/Rajmash	: *Phaseolus vulgaris*
Indian Cowpea/Lobia	: *Vigna unguiculata/V. sinensis* L.
Lentil	: *Lens esculantum/L. culinaris* Moench
Lathyrus/Chickling pea/ Grasspea	: *Lathyrus sativus*
Mothbean	: *Vigna/Phaseolus aconotifolia*
Horse gram/Kulthi	: *Macrotyloma uniflorum*
Edible Oilseed Crops	
Groundnut/Peanut/ Monkeynut	: *Arachis hypogea* L.
Sunflower	: *Helianthus annus* L.
Safflower	: *Carthamus tinctorius* L.
Rapseed and Mustard	: *Brassica* spp. L.
Sesamum/Til	: *Sesamum indicum* L.
Niger	: *Guzotta abssicinia*
Linseed/Flex	: *Linnum ussitatisimum* L.

Crops	Botanical Name
Non edible Oilseed Crops	
Castor	: *Ricinus communis* L.
Fiber Crops	
Cotton	: *Gossipium* spp.
Jute/tita pat	: *Corchorus capsularis*
Sunhemp	: *Crotolaria juncea* L.
Forage Crops	
Berseem	: *Trifolium alexandrinum* L.
Lucerne/Alfalfa	: *Medicago sativa* L.
Oat	: *Avena sativa* L.
Napier grass	: *Pennisetum purpureum* L.
Clusterbean/Gaur	: *Cymopsis tetragonalaba* L.
Sugar Crops	
Sugarcane/Cane	: *Saccharum officinarum* L.
Sugarbeet	: *Beta vulgaris* L.
Tuber Crops	
Potato	: *Solanum tuberosum* L.
Tapioca	: *Manihot utilissima*
Stimulate Crops	
Tobacco	: *Nicotiana* spp.
Opium	: *Papaver somniferum*
Medicinal Crops	
Safed musli	: *Chlorophytum borivilianum*
Ashwagandha/ Winter cherry	: *Withania somnifera*
Rouvolfia/Sarpagandha	: *Rouvolfia serpentina*
Isabgol	: *Plantago ovata*
Butch	: *Acorus calamus*
Bramhi	: *Bacopa morriei*
Nux vomica	: *Strychnos Nuxvomica*

Crops

	Botanical Name
Aromatic Crops	
Lemon grass	: *Cymbopogan flexuasus*
Mentha/Mint	: *Menthe arvensis*
Khus/Vetivar	: *Vetiveria zizanoides*
Citronella	: *Cymbopogan winterianus*
Tulsi/Basil	: *Ocimum sanctum*

D) Classification based on Special Purpose

1. **Arable crops:** Crops which are cultivated on ploughed land. They are annual crops and include cereals, root crops, tobacco, sugarcane, maize and potatoes.

2. **Aromatic crops:** The crop/plants contain odoriferous and volatile substances, which occur as essential oils, gum exudates; balsam and oleoresin in one or more part of plant, *viz.* wood, bark, foliage, flower and fruit are called Aromatic plants.

3. **Alley Crops:** Alley crops or *hedge-row intercrops* is grown under an agroforestry practice in which perennial, preferably leguminous trees or shrubs are grown simultaneously with arable crop. The trees, managed as hedgerows, are grown in wide rows and the crop is planted in the interspace or 'alley' between the tree rows. *e.g.* Sweet potato, Black gram, Turmeric and Ginger are grown in the passages formed by the rows of Eucalyptus, Subabul and Cassia etc.

4. **Augment Crops:** Such crops are grown to supplement the yield of the main crops. *e.g.* Japanese mustard with berseem.

5. **Avenue Crops:** Such crops are grown along farm roads and fences *e.g.* Pigeon pea, Glyricidia sisal etc.

6. **Border/Guard Crops:** Such crops protect another crops from trespassing of animals or restrict the speed of wind and are mainly grown as border *e.g.* safflower (thorny oilseed crop) is planted around the field of gram.

7. **Cash Crops:** A crop, such as tobacco, grown for direct sale rather than for livestock feed or a crop grown by a farmer primarily for sale to others rather than for his or her own use *e.g.* sugarcane, cotton, jute, tobacco etc.

8. **Catch/Contingent Crops:** Such crops are cultivated to catch the forthcoming season when main crop is failed *e.g.* Linseed, toria, urd, moong, cowpea

10. **Cover Crops:** A close-growing crop grown primarily to improve and protect the soil from erosion through their ground covering foliage and/or rootmats between periods of regular crop production *e.g.* Lobia, groundnut, urd, sweet potato, methi etc.

11. **Complementary Crops:** Both main and intercrop is benefited to each other *e.g.* Jowar + Lobia.

12. **Competitive Crops:** Such cops compete to each other and are unsuitable for intercropping *e.g.* two cereals.

13. **Exhaustive Crops:** These crops leave the field exhaustive after growing *e.g.* Cereals (Rice)

14. **Energy Crops:** An energy crop is a plant grown as a low cost and low maintenance harvest used to make biofuels, or directly exploited for its energy content e,g, sugarcane, potato, maize, topioca.

15. **Fouling Crops:** Such crops whose culture practices allow the infestation of weeds intensively *e.g.* direct seeded upland rice.

16. **Ley Crops:** Any crop or combination of crops is grown for grazing or harvesting for immediate or future feeding to livestock *e.g.* Berseem + Mustard.

17. **Medicinal crops**: The crop/plant contains alkaloids, glycosides, steroids or other groups of compounds of medicinal value, which is used commercially, such plants are called Medicinal plants.

18. **Mulch Crops**: Such crops are grown to conserve the soil moisture through their ground covering foliage *e.g.* cowpea.

19. **Nurse Crops:** A crop of trees (nurse trees), shrubs or other plants introduced to foster or nourishment of another crops by *i.e.* shading it, protecting it from frost, insolation or wind. The widest use of nurse crops is in the establishment of leguminaceous plants such as alfalfa, clover *e.g.* Sunhemp in sugarcane, Jowar in cowpea, Rai in pea.

20. **Paira/Utera Crops:** The seed of succeeding crops like lentil, gram, pea, Lathyrus, berseem, linseed etc. is sown broadcast at 10 to 15 days before harvesting rice crop. This practice saves time; money (to be spent on land preparation etc.) utilizes residual fertility. This practice is common in both upland and lowland rice culture.

21. **Paired row Crops:** Generally the third row of crop is removed or growing of crop in pair row and the third row is escaped with an object to conserve the soil moisture in Dryland areas.

22. **Restorative Crops:** Restorative crops are crops that help in maintaining the fertility of the soil, for *e.g.* pulses and legumes.

23. **Silage Crops:** Such crops like corn, legumes, and grasses that have been harvested at early maturity, finely chopped, packed tightly to exclude air, and stored in tower silos, pits, or trenches for properly fermentation which

is used as animal feed during lean period or offseason *e.g.* Maize, cowpea, Jowar etc.

24. **Smother Crops:** Smother crops are specialized cover crops being ability to suppress weeds by providing dense foliage and quick growing ability *e.g.* buckwheat, mustard, cowpea, urd etc.

25. **Stimulate Crops:** Stimulate crops stimulate the human body *e.g.* tobacco, opium etc.

26. **Supplementary Crops:** Such cops are neither complementary nor competitive *e.g.* maize + cucurbits.

27. **Trap Crops:** Trap crops are grown to protect the main cash crop from a certain pest or several pests. These crops are planted in completely surrounding the main cash crop and prevent pest attack from all sides of the field through attracting the pest *e.g.* cotton red bug trapped by Ladyfinger around cotton.

28. **Truck Crops:** Growing one or more vegetable crops on a large scale for fresh shipment to distant markets. Most important truck crops are Potato, tomatoes, lettuce, melons, beets, broccoli, celery, radishes, onions, cabbage, and strawberries.

E) Classification Based on Cultural Method/Water

1. **Rain fed:** crops grow only on rain water. *e.g.* Jowar, Bajara, Mung etc.

2. **Irrigated crops:** Crops grows with the help of irrigation water. *e.g.* Chilly, sugarcane, Banana, papaya etc.

F) Classification Based on Root System

1. **Tap root system:** The main root goes deep into the soil. *e.g.* Tur, Grape, Cotton etc.

2. **Adventitious/Fiber rooted:** The crops whose roots are fibrous shallow and spreading into the soil. *e.g.* Cereal crops, wheat, rice etc.

G) Classification Based on No. of Cotyledon

1. **Monocots or monocotyledons:** Having one cotyledon in the seed. *e.g.* all cereals and Millets.

2. **Dicots or dicotyledonous:** Crops having two cotyledons in the seed. *e.g.* all legumes and pulses.

(C) Effect of Weather Parameters on Crop Growth and Development

Different weather parameters affecting crop growth and development are following:

A) Solar Radiation

It is the primary source of energy on earth, and life depends on it. Solar radiation is defined as "The flux of radiant energy from the sun".

Importance of Light on Crop Plants

1. All the plant parts are directly or indirectly influenced by light.
2. Light of correct intensity, quality and duration is essential to normal plant development.
3. Poor light availability causes abnormalities and disorders in plants.
4. Light is indispensable to photosynthesis.
5. Light governs the distribution of photosynthates among different organs of plants.
6. Affects tiller production.
7. Affects stability, strength and length of culms.
8. Affects dry matter production.
9. Affects the size of the leaves.
10. Affects the root development.
11. Affects the flowering and fruiting.
12. Affects the dormancy of the seed.

B) Temperature

Temperature is defined as "The measure of speed per molecule of all the molecules of a body."

Importance of Air Temperature on Crop Plants

1. Temperature influences distribution of crop plants and vegetation.
2. The growth and development of crop plants are chiefly influenced by air temperature.
3. Affects leaf production, expansion and flowering.
4. Physical and chemical processes within the plants are governed by air temperature
5. The diffusion rate of gases and liquids changes with temperature
6. Solubility of different substances is dependent on temperature
7. Influences biochemical reactions in crops (double or triple with each 10°C rise)
8. Equilibrium of various systems and compounds in a function of temperature
9. Temperature affects the stability of enzymatic systems in the plants.

C) Atmospheric Pressure

Atmospheric pressure is defined as "The pressure exerted by a column of air with a cross sectional area of a given unit *i.e.,* a square inch or a square centimetre extending from the earth surface to the upper most boundary of the atmosphere".

D) Wind

Air in horizontal motion is known as "Wind". Winds are named by the direction they come from. Windward refers to the direction a wind comes from and leeward is the direction towards which it flows.

Importance of Wind Crop Plants

1. Transports heat in either sensible or latent form, from lower to higher latitudes.

2. Provides the moisture (to the land masses) which is necessary for precipitation.

3. Moderate turbulence promotes the consumption of carbon – dioxide by photosynthesis.

4. Wind prevents frost by disrupting a temperature inversion.

5. Wind dispersal of pollen and seeds is natural and necessary for certain agricultural crops, natural vegetation, etc. Example: The mountain and valley winds influence the soil temperature.

E) Evaporation and Condensation

The greater the rate of evaporation the more the soil is cooled. This is the reason for coolness of moist. Soil in windy conditions. On the other hand whenever water vapour from the atmosphere or from other soil depths condenses in the soil it heats up noticeable. Freezing of water generates heat.

F) Rainfall (Precipitation)

Depending on its temperature precipitation can either cool or warm the soil. Precipitation is defined as "Earthward falling of water drops or ice particles that have formed by rapid condensation in the atmosphere and are too large to remain suspended in the atmosphere".

Rain is defined as "Precipitation of drops of liquid water". The cloud consists of minute droplets of water and when these droplets combine and form large drops and can not remain suspended in the air they fall down as rain. These droplets are formed by rapid condensation. The size of rain drop is more than 0.5 mm in diameter. The imaginary lines drown on a map connecting the points of equal rainfall are known as "**Isohytes**".

Importance of Rainfall (Water) on Crop Plants

1. Water has high solvent power and this plays an important role in crop plants as the plants get their nourishment from soil only in solution form.

2. Water plays an important role in life processes of crop plants (in the exchange of gases).

3. The heat capacity of water is high and its high thermal stability helps in regulation of the temperature of crop plants.

4. Water has highest heat conduction capacity and due to this the heat produced by the activity of a cell is conducted immediately by water and distributed evenly to all plant parts.

5. The viscosity of water is higher than that of many solvents and this property helps in protecting the crop plants and trees against mechanical disturbances.

6. Water is driest at 4°C. The freezing point of fresh water being 0°C and that of sea water about – 2.5°C, the ice can float on the surface and plant life in deeper parts of sea is made possible.

7. The transparency of water facilitates the passage of light to great depths and this helps for the survival of aquatic plants.

8. The high surface tension that water has helps in movement of water into and through the plant parts.

9. Rainfall influences the distribution of crop plants in particular and vegetation in general, as the nature of vegetation of a particular place depends on the amount of rainfall (the vegetation of a desert where rainfall is less differs a lot from the vegetation of a rainforest).

H) Humidity

Humidity is an important factor in crop production and it is not an independent factor but closely related to rainfall and temperature. It plays significant role in weather and climate. The dampness of air is called humidity. Different types of humidity are as follows:

1. **Specific humidity:** It is defined as the ratio of the mass of water vapour in a sample of moist air to the total mass of the sample. It is expressed as kg of water vapour in a kg of moist air.

2. **Absolute humidity:** It is the ratio of the mass of water vapour to the volume of moist air in which it is contained. Absolute humidity is expressed as kg m^{-1}.

3. **Relative humidity:** It is expressed as the ratio of actual vapour pressure to the saturated pressure expressed in terms of percentage. It is most common measure of atmospheric humidity.

Effects of Humidity on crops

1. Humidity is the invisible vapour content of the air and is of great importance in determining the vegetation of a region.

2. It affects the internal water potential of plants.

3. Humidity is a major determinant of potential evapotranspiration. So, it determines the water requirement of crops.

4. It influences certain physiological phenomena including transpiration.

5. Change in relative humidity can produce various morphological and anatomical changes in the plants. For example, orchids grow abundantly in humid forests as epiphytes depend for their moisture supply on the atmosphere by developing certain morphological and anatomical characteristics that are not found in other plants (hydroscopic aerial roots).

6. Xerophytes in desert region where relative humidity is low show certain adaptations to conserve water.

7. High relative humidity can prolong the survival of crops under moisture stress.

8. Relative humidity plays a significant role in the outbreak of disease and pest epidemics. High humidity promoters the growth of some saprophytic and parasitic fungi and bacteria which cause various plant diseases.

9. Very high or very low relative humidity is not conductive for higher yields.

(D) Tillage and Tilth

☆ Jethro Till considered as **'Father of Tillage' Who Written'** Horse hoeing Husbandry' book.

☆ **Tillage:** It is the physical manipulation of soil with tools and implements to result in good tilth for better germination and subsequent growth of crops.

☆ Tillage of the soil consists of breaking the hard compact surface to a certain depth and other operations that are followed for plant growth. Tillage is the manipulation of soil with tools and implements for loosening the surface crust and bringing about conditions favourable for the germination of seeds and the growth of crops.

Types of Tillage

1. **Primary/Preparatory tillage**: The tillage operation which constitutes the initial measure soil working operation. It is normally design to reduce soil strength, cover plant material and rearrange aggregates and *mainly for seed bed preparation*. The main aim of primary plough is breaking, opening and turning of soil. The primary tillage implements are *Deshi plough*, MB plough, Ridge plough, Disk plough etc.

2. **Secondary tillage**: The tillage operation following primary tillage *to create a good seedbed for proper seeding/planting*. Lighter or finer operation performed on the soil after primary tillage are known as secondary tillage which includes the operations performed after ploughing, leveling, discing, harrowing etc. The secondary tillage implements are Cultivator, Harrows, Hoe, Planker, Roller etc.

Objectives of Tillage

1. To produce a satisfactory seed bed for good germination and good crop growth.
2. To make the soil loose and porous.
3. To aerate the soil.
4. To control weeds.
5. To remove the stubbles (that may harbour pests)
6. To expose the soil inhabiting pathogens and insect pests to sun and kill them.
7. To break hard pans in the soil.
8. For deep tillage and inversion of soil.
9. For incorporating bulky organic manures.
10. To warm up the soil.
11. To increase infiltration rate.

Tillage operations are grouped into two types based on the time at which they are carried out.

1. **Preparatory cultivation** – which is carried out before sowing the crop
2. **After cultivation** – That is practiced after sowing the crop.
   ❖ Primary tillage – Ploughing
   ❖ Secondary tillage – Harrowing
   ❖ Seed bed preparation – Country plough can be used.

Tillage Implements and their Works

1. Chisel plough — Subsoil breaking
2. Rotary plough — Cut and pulverizes the light soil
3. Ridge plough — Earthing-up and form ridges and furrows
4. Basin lister — Prevent runoff and form basins
5. Disc plough — Deep ploughing in grassed field
6. Tractor drawn cultivator — Destroy weeds and breaking clods
7. Sweep cultivator — Harvesting groundnut and used in stubble mulching
8. Harrows — Preparation of seedbed, destroy weeds
9. Planker — Micro levelling
10. Star weeder — Weeding in dry lands and groundnut
11. Potato digger — Used to harvest potatoes
12. Groundnut digger — Used to harvest groundnut

13. Groundnut Sheller — Used to separate kernels from the pods.

14. Maize Sheller — Used to separate maize grains from cobs.

TILTH

It is the good physical condition of soil resulting from tillage. A soil is said to be in good Tilth when it is soft, friable and properly aerated. The Tilth is the physical condition of the soil brought out by tillage that influences crop emergence, establishment, growth and development. Tilth is a loose, friable, airy, powdery granular and crumbly structure of the soil with optimum moisture content suitable for working and germination or sprouting seeds and propagates.

Characteristics of Good Tilth

1. A soil should be mellow, friable, crumbly and adequately aerated.

2. A soil in good tilth is porous. Capillary and non capillary pores are equal. This facilitates free movement of air and water.

3. Higher per cent of larger aggregates (more than 5 mm in diameter) are necessary for irrigated agriculture, while higher percentages of smaller aggregates (1 to 2 mm diameter) are desirable for dry land agriculture.

4. Tilth can be coarse or fine. For sandy soils fine kind of tilth is required and for heavy black soils rough cloddy conditions or coarse tilth is enough.

5. With very fine tilth, the surface gets caked up when it dries after a rain. Because of this, the soil is unable to absorb rain water and it results in runoff loses.

Modern Concepts of Tillage

Tillage is time consuming, laborious and costly, owing to this new concepts like minimum tillage and zero tillage are introduced.

1. Minimum Tillage

It is aimed at reducing tillage operations to the minimum necessary for ensuring a good seedbed, rapid germination, a satisfactory stand and favourable growing conditions, Tillage can be reduced by:

1) Omitting operations which do not give much benefit when compared to the cost and

2) Combining agricultural operations like seeding and fertilizer application.

Advantages

1. Improve soil condition due to decomposition of plant residues *in situ*.

2. Higher infiltration caused by decomposition of vegetation present on Soils and channels formed by decomposition of dead roots.

3. Less resistance to root growth due to improved structure.

4. Less soil compaction by reduced movement of heavy tillage vehicles.

5. Less soil erosion compared to conventional tillage.

Disadvantages

1. Less seed germination,

2. More 'N' has to be added as rate of decomposition of organic matter is slow.

3. Nodulation may affect in some legumes.

4. Sowing operations are difficult with ordinary implements.

2. Zero Tillage

It is an extreme form of minimum tillage. Primary tillage is completely avoided and secondary tillage is restricted to seedbed preparation in the row zone only. It is followed where:

1. Soils are subjected to wind and water erosion,

2. Timing of tillage operations is too difficult &

3. Requirements of energy and labour for tillage are too high.

Advantages

1. Soils are homogenous in structure with more no. of earth worms.

2. Organic matter content increased due to less mineralization.

3. Surface runoff is reduced due to presence of mulch. Several operations are performed by using only one implement. In these weeds are controlled by spraying of herbicides.

Disadvantages

1. Higher 'N' is too applied due to slower mineralization of org. matter.

2. Large population of perennial weeds appears.

3. Build up of pests is more.

3. Conservation Tillage

It is disturbing the soil to the minimum extent and leaving crop residues on the soil. It includes minimum and zero tillage which can reduce soil loss up to 99 per cent over conventional tillage. In most cases, it reduces soil by 50 per cent over conventional tillage. Conventional tillage includes ploughing twice or thrice followed by harrowing and planking. It leaves no land unploughed and leaves no residues on the soil.

PUDDLING

Puddling operation consists of ploughing repeatedly in standing water until the soil becomes soft and muddy. Initially, 5cm to 10 cm of water is applied depending on the water status of the soil to bring it to saturation and above and the first ploughing is carried out.

(E) Soil-Water Plant Relationship

Soil-Water

a) Water has maximum density at 4^0C. One molecule of water is attached to four molecules in the neighbourhood.

b) The surface tension of water is 72.7 dyne/cm^2 at 25^0C.

c) **Available water**: The range of available water that can be stored in soil and be available for growing crops is known as available soil water/moisture. This water is held between $1/3^{rd}$ and 15 atm.

d) *"The difference between the amount of water in the soil at field capacity and the amount at the permanent wilting point referred to as the available water or moisture".*

e) The water is readily absorbed by the plant roots between Field capacity (-0.33 bar) to Permanent wilting point (-15 bar).

1) Field Capacity

✰ Field capacity is the amount of soil moisture or water content held in soil after excess water has drained away and the rate of downward movement has materially decreased, which usually takes place within 2–3 days after a rain or irrigation in pervious soils of uniform structure and texture.

✰ Field capacity (FC) is the amount of water that a soil can hold against drainage by gravity.

✰ This usually occurs between 1/10 atm. (coarse soils) and 1/3 atm. (heavy soil).

✰ Field capacity is considered as upper limit of available water.

✰ Field capacity is characterised by measuring water content after wetting a soil profile, covering it (to prevent evaporation) and monitoring the change in soil moisture in the profile. Water content when the rate of change is relatively small is indicative of when drainage ceases and is called *Field Capacity*, it is also termed *drained upper limit* (DUL).

2) Permanent Wilting Point☐(PWP) or☐Wilting Point☐(WP)

✰ The soil moisture content at which the plant will wilt and die. While there still may be water in the soil, the plant is not able to extract sufficient water from the soil to meet its needs.

✰ Permanent wilting point is the moisture content in a soil at which plants permanently wilt and will not recover. This occurs between 10 and 20 atm. of tension.

✰ PWP is considered as lower limit of available water.

Kinds of Soil Water

1. Gravitational water
2. Capillary water
3. Hygroscopic water

1. **Gravitational water:** Water in the micropores that moves downward freely under the influence of gravity (< 1/3 bar) beyond the root zone is called gravitational water. It is not available to plants.

2. **Capillary water:** Water retained by the soil in capillary pores (micropores), against gravity (-1/3 to -31 bar) by the force of surface tension as continues film around soil particles is called capillary water. It is available for plant growth.

3. **Hygroscopic water:** When water is held tightly as thin film around soil particles by adsorption forces and no longer moves in capillary pores, is called hygroscopic water. It flows at gravity of > -31 bar.

Water Requirements (WR) of Crops

"Water requirements of a crop is the quantity of water needed for normal crop growth and yield in a period of time to a place and may be supplied by precipitation or by irrigation or by both."

Water is needed mainly to meet the demand of evaporation (E), transpiration (T) and metabolic activity of plant together known as **consumptive use** (C.U.)

So, **WR = Irrigation water + Effective rainfall + Soil profile contribution**
    (IW, in cm)   (ER, in cm)   (S)

Water Requirement of Different Crops

Sl.No.	Crops	Water Requirement (cm)
1.	Rice	90-250
2.	Wheat, Sorghum, Soybean, Tobbaco	45-65
3.	Maize, Groundnut	50-80
4.	Sugarcane	150-250
5.	Soybean	45-70
6.	Cotton	70-130
7.	Potato	60-80

The period when water requirement is maximum is called as **peak period of water requirement/critical stages.**

Critical Stages of Crops for Irrigation

Cereals

1.	Rice	:	Tillering, Panicle Initiation, Heading and Flowering
2.	Wheat	:	CRI, Tillering, Late jointing, Flowering, milking and dough stage
3.	Maize	:	Tasseling and Silking to Dough Stage
4.	Sorghum	:	Booting, Blooming, Milking and Dough Stage
5.	Pearl millet	:	Heading and Flowering
6.	Finger millet	:	Primordial Initiation and Flowering

Pulses

1.	Chickpea	:	Late vegetative phase and Pod development
2.	Pea	:	Flowering and Early pod formation
3.	Black gram	:	Flowering and Pod setting
4.	Greengram	:	Flowering and Pod setting
5.	Lucerne	:	After cutting and Flowering
6.	Beans	:	Flowering and Pod setting

Oilseeds

1.	Groundnut	:	Flowering, Peg formation and Pod development
2.	Soybean	:	Blooming and Seed formation
3.	Sunflower	:	Buttoning, Knee high, Flowering and Early seed formation
4.	Sesamum	:	Blooming to Maturity

(F) Weed Management

☆ First person to use the term weed is *'Jethro Tull'*

Definition of Weeds

1. A weed is a plant growing where it is not desired.
2. Weed is an unwanted plant.
3. A plant with negative value.
4. A plant interferes with intended use of land.
5. A plant growing with desired plant.

Characteristics of Weeds

1. **Prolific seed production**: *Amaranthus* spp. - 1,96,000 seeds/plant

   Chenopodium sp.- 72,000 seeds/plant

2. **Dormancy in seed**: *Chenopodium* sp. - 20-25 years, *Phalaris minor* - 4-5 years

3. **Competitiveness and Agressiveness**: High and fast growth rate, having higher leaf area

4. **Vegetative propogated**: Propagated by rhizomes, bulbs, tubers, stolens, suckers etc.

5. **Morphological similarities:** *Phalaris minor* in wheat and *Echinochloa* sp. in rice

6. **Deep root system:** Roots of *Convolvulus* sp. has up to 20 feet deep roots, whereas *Cyperus rotundus* has 5-7 feet deep.

7. **Early seed setting and early maturity**

8. **Evasiveness**

Importance/Benefits of Weeds with Example

1. **Maintain soil fertility**: *Typha* spp. (add 1-35 per cent nitrogen)

2. **Control soil erosion**: *Cynodon dactylon, Convolvulus arvensis*

3. **Used as fodder**: *Cichorium intybus, Cynodon* spp.

4. **Have medicinal value**: *Leucas aspera* is used in snake bite; *Striga* spp. is used in diabetes; *Phyllanthus niruri* is used in Jaundice; *Argemone maxicana* is used in skin disease

5. **Have economical value**: Roots of *Cichorium intybus* is used in adding flavour to coffee; *Cyperus rotundus* is used in making agarbatti; *Saccharum spontaneum* is used in roof making

6. **Maintain pH**: *Argemone maxicana* is used for making alkaline soil to acidic; *Rumex acetocella* is used for making acidic soil to alkaline

7. **Used as ornamental plants**: *Lantana camara, Eichhornia crassipes*

8. **Used in cleaning water**: *Eichhornia crassipes*

9. **Adds organic matter to soil**: *Amaranthus viridis, Convolvulus arvensis*

10. **Used as vegetables**: *Chenopodium album, Amaranthus viridis*

11. **Religious purpose**: *Cynodon* spp.

12. **Useful for cottage industries**: *Saccharum spontaneum, Typha* spp.

13. **Donating genes to crop plants (crop breeding)**: *Saccharum spontaneum* (used in sugarcane)

14. **Used as nematicides**: *Crotolaria, Parthenium*

15. **Used as pollution indicator**: *Brassica kaber* (Wild mustard) to indicate NO_2 pollution; *Stellaria redia* (Chick weeds) to indicate SO_2 pollution

Losses Due to Weeds

1. Weeds compete with crop plants for resource like light, moisture, nutrients and space.
2. Weeds cause reduction in crop yields. Among the annual agriculture loss in India, weeds accounts for 45 per cent, insects 30 per cent, diseases 20 per cent others 5 per cent.
3. Weeds increase cost of cultivation.
4. Weeds are alternate hosts for crop pests and diseases.
5. Weeds reduce the quality of produce. *e.g.* Cuscuta as an admixture with Lucerne spoils seed quality.
6. Wild onion and wild garlic as weeds in fodder crops impart off-flavour to milk.
7. Xanthium impairs wool quality of sheep.
8. Weeds cause human health problems. *e.g.* Allergy by Parthenium hysterophorus, Hay fever and asthma caused by *Franseria* sp., Dermatitis caused by Amrosia and Helenium, Itching and inflammations caused by hair of *Urtica* sp.
9. Weeds cause animal health problems also. Ex. Lantana camara induces hypersensitivity to light., *Rhododendron* sp. cause diarrhoea and blood strains in milk. Sorghum halepense poisonous to cattle.
10. Problems of water contamination. *e.g.* Reduce flow of water in irrigation channels, Reduce flow of water in irrigation channels. *e.g. Eichornia typha*.
11. Reduction in land value, due to *Cyperus rotundus* and *Cynodon dactylon*.
12. Allelopathy: Harmful affects of plant due to research and phytochemicals on other plants.
13. Avena fatua: Affect germination of weed. Seed exudates.

Classification of Weeds

A) Basis of Life Cycle

Annual: a) Kharif: *Eleusine, Echinochloa, Celosia, Cyperus*

b) Rabi : *Argemone, Phalaris, Chenopodium, Euphorbia, Solanum* sp.

Binnial: *Dacus carota, Cirsium vulgare, Alternanthera pungens*

Perrenial: *Cyperus rotundus, Convolvolus, Cynodon* sp., *Ageratum conizoids, Achyranthus, Saccharum spontanium, Zyziphus rotundifolia*

B) Basis of Site of Predominance

1. **Obligate weeds** : Such weeds are grown in cultivated field, *e.g. Anagallis, Chenopodium*
2. **Facultative weeds**: Grown both in wild and cultivated field, *e.g. Argemone, Euphobia*

C) Basis of Parasitic Nature

Parasitic Nature		Weed	Host Crop/Plant
1. Semi root	:	*Striga* spp.	Sorghum and Sugarcane
2. Semi stem	:	*Loranthus* spp.	Mango
3. Total root	:	*Orabanchi* spp.	Tobacco
4. Total stem	:	*Cuscuta* spp.	Lucerne

D) Basis of Morphological Characteristics

1. **Grasses**: All graminaceous weeds, *e.g. Avena, Cynodon, Echinochloa* spp.
2. **Sedges**: All weeds belong to Cyperaceae family, *e.g. Cyperus* spp.
3. **Broad leafy**: All dicot weeds, *e.g. Chenopodium, Camellina* etc.

E) Basis of Season

1. **Annual**: *Avena, Amaranthus, Argemone, Celosia, Echinochloa, Chenopodium* etc.
2. **Binnial**: *Eichornia intybus, Alternanthera echinata* etc.
3. **Perenial**: *Zizyphus rotundifolis, Cynodon* etc.

F) Other Basis

1. Relative weeds : Rice in wheat field.
2. Absolute weeds : *Cyperus rotundus*
3. Rogue : The off type crop varieties
4. Mimicry weeds : *Phalaris* in wheat field, wild rice in rice field
5. Noxious weeds : *Parthenium* sp. (difficult to control)
6. Objectionable weeds : *Convolvulus arvensis* and *Phalaris* in wheat and wild rice in rice
7. Associated weeds : *Phalaris minor* and *Avena fatua* in wheat, *Echinochloa* spp. in rice

Important Weeds of Different Crops

A) Kharif Crops

1.	Paddy	:	*Echinochloa* spp., *Cyperus* spp., *Wild rice, Celosia* sp., *Eclipta, Cynodon* sp.
2.	Maize, Sorghum, Bajra	:	*Phyllanthus* sp., *Amaranthus* sp., *Johnson grass, Cynodon* sp., *Cyperus* spp., *Partulaca* sp.
3.	Soybean, Moong, Urd, Arhar, Groundnut and Cotton	:	*Phyllanthus* sp., *Solanum nigrum, Amaranthus* sp., *Wild oat, Johnson grass, Celosia* sp., *Kodo, Cynodon* sp., *Cyperus* spp., *Partulaca* sp.

B) Rabi crops

1.	Wheat and Barley	:	*Chenopodium* sp., *Anagallis* sp., *Phalaris minor,* *Wild oat, Melilotus* spp., *Cynodon* sp., *Cyperus* spp., *Convolvulus* sp., *Vicia hirsute, Asphodelus* sp.
2.	Gram, Pea, Lentil, Potato, Mustard and Linseed	:	*Fumaria parviflora, Anagallis* sp., *Chenopodium* sp., *Melilotus* sp., *Asphodelus* sp., *Cynodon* sp., *Cyperus* spp., *Convolvulus* sp., *Vicia hirsute, Wild safflower,* *Cyperus* spp., *Argemone maxicana*
3.	Berseem	:	*Chicorium intybus, Cynodon, Anagallis, Cyperus* spp.
4.	Tobacco	:	*Orobanche* sp., *Melilotus* sp., *Convolvulus* sp., *Cynodon, Cyperus* spp.
5.	Sugarcane	:	Most of kharif and rabi weeds

Critical Period of Crop – Weed Competition

Competition is struggle between two organisms for a limited resource that is essential for growth. Water, nutrient, light and space are the major factors for which usually competition occurs. Competition between crop plants and weeds is most severe when they have similar vegetative habit and common demand for available growth factors. Weeds appear much more adapted to agro-ecosystems than our crop plants. Without interference by man, weeds would easily wipe out the crop plants. Generally, an increase in on kilogram of weed growth will decrease one kilogram of crop growth.

1. "The shortest time span during the crop growth when weeding results in highest economic returns"

2. The crop yield level obtain by weeding during this period is almost similar to that obtained by the full season weed free competition.

3. It is the period of crop growth during which weeds cause great loss to the crop and this is the period during which the crop has to be maintained in a weed free environment. Weed competition is severe in early stages of crop growth. Generally crops must be maintained weed free during the first 1/3rd period of life cycle.

Crops	Critical Period (days)	Reduction in Grain Yield (per cent)
(A) Cereals		
Paddy - Direct sown	20-45	15-90
- Transplanting	30-45	15-40
Upland condition	Entire period	40-90

Crops	Critical Period (days)	Reduction in Grain Yield (per cent)
Wheat	30-45	20-40
Maize	15-45	40-60
Sorghum	15-45	15-40
Pearlmillet	30-45	15-60
(B) Pulses		
Pigeonpea	15-60	20-40
Green gram	15-30	25-50
Black gram	15-30	30-50
Cow pea	15-30	15-30
Chickpea	30-60	15-25
Peas	30-45	20-30
Lentil	30-60	20-30
(C) Oilseed		
Soybean	20-45	40-60
Groundnut	40-60	40-50
Sunflower	30-45	30-60
Castor	30-50	30-35
Safflower	15-45	15-40
Sesamum	15-45	15-40
Rapeseed mustard	15-40	15-30
Linseed	20-45	30-40
(D) Commercial crops		
Sugarcane	30-120	20-30
Potato	20-40	30-60
Cotton	15-60	40-50
Jute	30-45	50-80
(E) Vegetable crops		
Cauliflower	30-45	50-60
Cabbage	30-45	50-60
Okra	15-30	40-50
Tomato	30-45	40-70
Onion	30-75	60-70

Principles of Crop Weed Competition

1. Competition for nutrients
2. Competition for moisture
3. Competition for light
4. Competition for CO_2

1. Competition for Nutrients

It is an important aspect of crop weed competition. Weeds usually absorb mineral nutrients faster than crop plants. Usually weeds accumulate relatively larger amounts of nutrients than crop plant Nutrient removal by weeds leads to huge loss of nutrients in each crop season, which is often twice that of crop plants.

Amaranthus accumulate over 3 per cent nitrogen in their dry matter and this fall under category of **nitrophylls**. *Digetaria* spp. accumulates more phosphorous content of over 3.36 per cent. *Chenopodium* and *Portuluca* are potassium lovers, with over 4.0 per cent K_2O in their dry matter. *Setaria lutescens* accumulates as high as 585 ppm of zinc in its dry matter. This is about three times more than by cereal crop.

2. Competition for Moisture

Crop weed competition becomes critical with increasing soil moisture stress. In general **for producing equal amount of dry matter weeds transpire more water than field crops.** Therefore, the actual evapotranspiration from the weedy crop fields is much more than the evapotranspiration from a weed free crop field. Consumptive use of *Chenopodium album* is 550mm as against 479mm for wheat crop. Further it was noted that weeds remove moisture evenly from up to 90 cm soil depth. While the major uptake of moisture by wheat was limited to top 15 cm of soil depth. Weeds growing in fallow land are found to consume as much as 70- 120 ha mm of soil moisture and this moisture is capable of producing 15 -20 q of grain per ha in the following season.

3. Competition for Light (Solar Energy)

Plant height and vertical leaf area distribution are the important elements of crop weed competition. When moisture and nutrients in soil are plentiful, weeds have an edge over crop plants and grow taller. **Competition for light occurs during early crop growth** season if a dense weed growth smothers the crop seedlings. Crop plants suffer badly due to shading effect of weeds. Cotton, potato several vegetables and sugarcane are subjected to heavy weed growth during seedling stage. Unlike competition for nutrients and moisture once weeds shade a crop plant, increased light intensity cannot benefit it.

4. Competition for Space (CO_2)

Crop-weed competition for space is the requirement for CO_2 and the competition may occur under extremely crowded plant community condition. A more efficient utilization of CO_2 by C4 type weeds may contribute to their rapid growth over C3 type of crops.

☆ Factors affecting weed-crop interference or critical period of crop weed competition:

1. Period of weed growth.

2. Weeds/crop density.

3. Plant species effects. a) Weed species b) Crop species and varieties.

4 Soil and climatic influence: (a) Soil fertility, (b) Soil moisture status, (c) Soil reaction and (d) Climatic influences.

5. Cropping practices: (a) Time and method of planting crops (b) Method of planting of Crops (c) Crop density and rectangularity.

Weed Control Methods

Broadly classified in two groups:

A) Preventive Measures

B) Curative or Control Measures which includes:

    i. Mechanical

    ii. Cropping or Cultural

    iii. Biological and

    iv. Chemical

A. Preventive Measures

In this, the weeds are prevented from its multiplication, introduction and nipped off the buds. It consists of:

1. Use clean seed

2. Use well decomposed FYM/Compost

3. Cut the weeds before seeding

4. Remove weed growth or keep irrigation and drainage channels clean or free from seeds

5. Avoid feeding of grain screenings, hay or fodder containing weed seeds without destroying their viability by grinding or cooking

6. Avoid use of sand or soil from weed infested areas to clean or cultivated areas

7. Avoid allowing castles to move from weed infested areas to clean or cultivated areas

8. Clean all the farm implements and machinery properly after their use in infested areas and before using in clean areas

9. Keep farm fences, roads and bunds clean or free from weeds

10. Watch seedlings in nurseries carefully so that they do not get mixed with weed seedlings and get carried to the fields.

B. Curative Measures

These measures are followed to remove or to smother the weed growth and further multiplication. It includes:

I) Mechanical/Physical methods

It comprises:

1) Hand pulling
2) Hand weeding
3) Burning
4) Flooding
5) Hoeing
6) Tillage
7) Moving
8) Smothering with non-living material (mulching). Burning of seed bed is called as 'rabbing'.

II) Cropping/Cultural Methods

"One who establish first/early, will suppress other." Therefore, the cultural practices are so managed that the crop plants should establish early and grow faster ahead of the weeds. **It includes:**

1) **Crop rotations:** It checks the free growth of weed due to change of crops season to season.

2) **Kind of crop:** Groundnut covering crops like legumes will smother the weed growth. *e.g.* Sunhemp, Groundnut etc.

3) **Use of fertilizers:** Application of optimum doses of fertilizers to crop will help to grow faster.

4) **Date and rate of planting or sowing:** Sowing of crops at proper time with optimum seed rate will help the crop to cover the ground and will make the weeds deprive of light.

III) Biological Methods

It includes the use of living organisms for suppressing or controlling the weeds. Plant, animal or micro organisms may be used for destruction of weeds. These are called as **bioagents** which feed on only the weeds and not on crop plants. *e.g.*: Prickly pear or Nagphana weed in South India was controlled by Conchineal insects. (*Dactlopius tomentosus*). In Australia (Hawaii Islands) several kinds of moths were used to control *Lantana Camara* which eats the flowers and fruits. This method is very efficient and economical provided right type of predators, parasites or pathogens which even under starvation conditions will not feed upon cultivated crops are found out and introduced.

Biological Control of Weeds

	Weeds	Bio-agent	Remark
1.	*Lantana camara*	*Crosidosema lantani*	A moth
2.	*Opuntia* spp. (Cactus)	*Cactoblastic cactorum*	An Insect
3.	*Cyperus rotundus*	*Bactra varutana*	Shoot boring moth
4.	*Eichornia crassipes*	*Rhizoctonia solani*	A fungus
5.	*Orabanchi* spp.	*Sclerotia* spp.	A fungus
6.	*Xanthium stramarium*	*Nupserha vextor*	A beetle
7.	Aquatic weeds	Chinese grass carp (*T. idella*)	Grass carp fish
8.	*Parthenium hysteroforus*	*Cassia cerassia/tora* *Zygrogramma bicolarata*	Competitive plant Mexican beetle
9.	Water hycinth	*Neochetina* spp.	—

Commercialized Bio-herbicides

	Product	Content	Target Weeds Controlled
1.	DEVINE	*Phytophthora palmivora*	Strangle vine
2.	BIPOLARIS	*Bipolaris sorghicola*	Johnson grass
3.	COLLEGO/	*Colletrotrichum gloesporiodes*	*Saccharum spontanium*
4.	TRIPOSE	*Shrimp*	*Echinochloa* spp. in rice
5.	DR. BIO SEDGE	*Puccinia coriculata*	*Cyperus esculentus*
6.	LUBOE-2	*Colletrotrichum gloesporiodes*	*Cuscuta reflexa*
7.	VELGO	*Colletrotrichum coccoids*	Volvet leaf in soybean and maize
8.	BIOMAL	*Colletrotrichum gloesporiodes* f.sp. *malvae*	*Cassia obtusifolia*
9.	ABG 500B	*Cercospora rodmanii*	*Abutilon theopharsti*
10.	CASST	*Alternaria cassiae*	*Morrenia odorata*

IV) Chemical Methods

This is very effective in certain cases and has a great scope provided the chemicals are cheap, efficient and easily available. The chemicals used for weed control and which suppress or destroy the growth of weeds, called as *herbicide*. These either help in killing the weeds or in inhibiting their growth. *e.g.* 2, 4-D, Atrazine, Glyphosate, etc.

Types of Herbicide

1. **Selective herbicides** are those which kill only weeds without injuring crop plants. *e.g.* 2,4-D, Simazine, Atrazine, Butachlor, Pendimethalin etc.

2. **Non-selective herbicides** are those which kill all kinds of vegetations *i.e.* weed and crop plant. *e.g.* Diquat, Paraquat, Fenoxaprop-ethyl etc.

3. **Contact herbicides** kill all the plant parts which may get covered by the chemical by directly killing the plant cells. These chemicals are effective against annuals particularly when they are young but not perennials. *e.g.* Most of non-selective herbicides.

4. **Translocated/Systemic herbicides** are first absorbed in the foliage or through roots and are then translocated to other parts of the plant. Or Kill plants after their absorption by accelerating or retarding the metabolic activities of plants. These are more effective in destroying deep rooted perennials. *e.g.* Most of selective herbicides.

Based on relative time of application to weed emergence, the herbicides are classified as:

1. Pre-plant applied (Before planting of crop)

2. Pre-emergence (Before emergence of weeds)

3. Post-emergence (After emergence of weeds)

1. Pre-emergence Treatment or Application of Herbicides

Application of herbicides after sowing of crop but before emergence of crop and weeds is called **pre-emergence application.** It is done from first to fourth day of sowing and only selective herbicides are used. Generally germinating weeds are killed by pre-emergence application and gives competitive advantage of crop. *e.g.*: Pre-emergence application of Atrazine @ 0.5 to 2.5 kg/ha in sugarcane, Jowar, Alachlor @ 1.5 to 2.5 kg ai/ha in Groundnut, Oxadiazon @ 1.5 kg ai/ha in cotton.

2. Post-emergence Application of Herbicides

Application of herbicides after emergence of crop is called **post-emergence application.** It is generally resorted to when the crop has grown sufficiently to tolerate herbicides and to kill weeds that appear late in the crop. Generally, it is done about 30-40 days after sowing. For example, application of Stam F34 @ 2 kg/ha or MCR 1 kg/ha in paddy 3 weeks after transplanting, 2,4-D @ 0.4 kg/ha in Wheat after 4-8 leaf stage, Pendimethalin @ 0.75 to 2.0 kg ai/ha in rice after 3-5 DAT, Isoproturon @ 1.0 kg ai/ha 30 – 35 days after sowing of Wheat.

(G) Cropping Systems

It is an order in which the crops are cultivated on a piece of land over a fixed period this is cropping system. Or it can be defined as "The cropping pattern used on a farm and its interactions with farm resources, other farm enterprises and available technology which determine their makeup".

Monocropping

or Monoculture refers to growing of only one crop on a piece of land year after year.

e.g. Rice – Rice (In Godavari belt)

Disadvantage in Monocropping

1. Improper use of moisture and nutrients from the soil

2. Control of crop associated pests and weeds become a problem.

Crop Rotation

It is a process of growing different crops in succession on a piece of land in a specific period of time with an object to get maximum profit from least investment without impairing soil fertility.

1. Crop rotation is the reverse of land rotation. In this, crop is rotated year after year.

2. The main objective of crop rotation is to maintain and even improves soil fertility and stabilize income.

Principles of Crop Rotation

1. The crops with tap roots should be fall by those which have a fibrous root system.

2. The leguminous crops should be grown after non leguminous crops.

3. More exhaustive crops should be followed by less exhaustive crop.

4. Selection of crops should be demand based.

5. Selection of crops should be problem based.

6. The crops of the same family should not be grown in succession because the act like alternate host for insects, pests and disease pathogens.

7. An ideal crop rotation is one which provides maximum employment to the family and farm labour, the machines and equipments are efficiently used then all the agriculture operations are done simultaneously.

Overlapping System of Cropping

In this the succeeding crop is sown in standing proceeding crop thus in this system, before harvesting one crop the seeds of next crop are sown. *e.g.* Maize - potato – onion - bendi in North India.

Ratoon Cropping

It refers to raising a crop with re growth coming out of roots or stalks after harvest of the crop. *e.g.* Sugarcane.

Multi Storeyed System

Growing of plants of different heights in same field at the same time is termed as multistoreyed cropping. *e.g.* Coconut – Piper - Banana – Pineapple.

Cropping Pattern

The yearly sequence and spatial arrangement of crops or of crop and fallow on a given area, or Crop rotation practiced by the majority of the farmers in a given area or locality.

    A) Rice based cropping pattern: Rice - Wheat

    B) Wheat based cropping pattern: Rice – Wheat, Pigeonpea – Wheat, Moong – Wheat etc.

Farming System

An appropriate combination of farm enterprises *viz.* cropping system, livestock, poultry, fisheries and the means available to the farmer to raise them for increasing profitability.

Mixed Farming

1. A system of farming on a particular farm which includes crop production, raising livestock, poultry, fisheries, bee keeping etc. to sustain and safety as many needs of the farmer as possible. The objective is subsistence while higher profitability without altering ecological balance is important in farming system.

2. Cropping pattern which involve the raising of crops, animals and or trees.

Live Mulch System

Live mulch crop production involves planting a food crop directly into a living cover of an established cover crop without tillage or the destruction of the fallow vegetation.

Sole Cropping/Solid Planting

1. It is opposite of intercropping.

2. *"One crop variety grown alone in pure stands at normal density in a field"*.

Multiple Cropping

Growing two or more crops on the same piece of land in one agriculture year is known as '*Multiple cropping*'. It is the intensification of cropping in time and space dimensions *i.e.*, more number of crops with in a year and more number of crops on the same piece of land.

Types of Multiple Cropping

    a) Inter cropping

    b) Mixed cropping

c) Sequential/non-overlapped cropping

d) Relay/overlapped cropping

a) Intercropping

"Growing of two or more crops simultaneously in alternate rows or otherwise in the same area, where there is significant amount of inter crop competition".

e.g. Setaria + Redgram (5:1 ratio)

Groundnut + Redgram (7:1 ratio)

Advantages of Intercropping

a) Greater stability of yield over different seasons,

b) Better use of growth resources,

c) Better control of weeds, pests and diseases,

d) One crop provides physical support to the other crop,

e) One crop provides shelter to the other crop,

f) Erosion control through providing continuous leaf cover over the ground surface, and

g) It is the small farmers of limited means who is most likely to benefit.

Disadvantages of Intercropping

a) Yield decrease because of adverse competition effect,

b) Allelopathic effect,

c) Creates obstruction in the free use of machines for intercultural operations, and

d) Large farmers with adequate resources may likely to get less benefit out of intercropping.

b) Mixed Cropping

Cultivation of two or more than two crops simultaneously on the same piece of land without any definite row pattern or fixed ratio.

1. Scientific study of mixed cropping was firstly done by La-Flitze in 1929.

2. Mixed cropping is commonly practiced in Dryland areas of India.

3. Sowing of seeds is generally by broadcasting method.

4. Main objective is to lessen the risk of total crop failture, and to satisfy the farmers in food and fodder.

5. Mixed cropping needs irrigation through out the year.

c) Sequential/Non-Overlapped Cropping

Growing of two or more crops in quick succession on the same piece of land in a farming year. The swing of the succeeding crop and harvesting of the preceeding crop may be done simultaneously or in a quick succession *e.g.* Just after the harvest of Maize, Potato is sown and just after digging of potato, Chilli is sown.

d) Relay/Overlapped Cropping

Relay planting is inter-planting or inter sowing of seeds/seedlings of the succeeding crop before harvesting the preceeding/maturing crop.

1. Generally 2nd crop is planted after the first crop has reach its reproductive stage of growth *e.g.* Potato is planted before the harvest of Maize and Radish is sown before harvesting of Potato.

2. Paira (Bihar and WB) and Utera (MP) cropping are also referred as an example of relay cropping. Paira/Utera cropping means sowing of Lathyrus or Lentil before the harvest of rice in lowland area with an objective to use the residual moisture of rice field.

Multi Storeyed/Multitired/Multilevel Cropping

Two or more than two crops of different heights cultivated simultaneously on the same field. It is generally practised in Karnataka and Kerala. *e.g.* Sugarcane + Mustard + Onion/Potato.

Parallel Cropping

Such crops have different growth habits and zero competition to each other.

e.g. Urd/Moong + Maize

Companion Cropping

When the productions of both inter crops is equal to that of its solid planting.

e.g. Mustard/Potato/Onion + Sugarcane

Synergetic Cropping

In this type of cropping, yield of both the crops are higher than their pure crops on unit area. *e.g.* Sugarcane + Potato.

Cropping Index

The number of crops grown per annum on a given area of land multiplied by hundred.

Land Equivalent Ratio

Ratio of the area needed under sole cropping to one of intercropping at the same management level to give an equal amount to yield. LER is the sum of the fractions of the yield of the intercrops, relative to their sole crop yields. Intercropping system says advantageous, when LER is more than 1.0

Chapter 3
Horticulture

(A) Definition and Scope of Horticulture

☆ The term **"Horticulture"** is derived from two Latin words **'Hortus'** means **'Garden or enclosure'** and **'Culture'** means **'Cultivation**. So horticulture literally means garden culture or culture of garden crops.

Definition of Horticulture

1. "Horticulture crops include fruits, vegetables, flowers, plantation crops, spices, condiments, medicinal and aromatic crops etc".

2. Horticulture may be broadly defined as the Science and art of growing fruits, vegetables and flowers and crops like spices condiments and other plantation crops.

3. Horticulture deals with the raising of trees for shade, ornamental and avenue purposes, planning and raising of ornamental gardens, parks and raising of seed and planting material. Further, horticulture also deals with the utilization of horticulture produce and improvement of horticulture crops.

Branches of Horticulture

Based upon the crops dealt and also their purpose and utilization, the branch of horticulture is sub-divided in to the following branches:

A) Main Branches

Sl.No.	Branch		Description
1.	Pomology	:	It deals with cultivation of fruit crops.
2.	Olericulture	:	It deals with cultivation of vegetable crops.

Sl.No.	Branch		Description
3.	Floriculture	:	It deals with cultivation of ornamental flowers and land scaping.
4.	Fruit and vegetable preservation	:	It deals with the principles of fruit and vegetable preservation.

B) Sub Branches

1. Plantation and Medicinal plants.
2. Ornamental Gardening
3.
   Landscape gardening and
4. Nursery plant production

1. Pomology

It is derived from two words *i.e.* **Pomum** meaning **fruit** and **Logos** means **discourse or study**. So, pomology is study or cultivation of fruit crops. *e.g.* Mango, Sapota, Guava, Grape, Banana etc.

2. Olericulture

It is derived from two words *i.e.* **Oleris** means **Potherb** and **Culture** means cultivation. So, Olericulture literally means **potherb** cultivation. In the present days it is broadly used to indicate the cultivation of vegetables. *e.g.* Brinjal, Okra, Tomato, Pumpkin etc.

3. Floriculture

It is derived from two words *i.e.* Florus meaning flower and Culture meaning cultivation. So floriculture means study of flower crops. In this there are again two sub-divisions. (1) Commercial Floriculture (2) Ornamental Floriculture.

A. ***Commercial floriculture:*** Deals with the cultivation of flower crops grown on commercial scale for profit (Income). *e.g.*: Rose, Jasmine, Carnation, Aster and Marigold etc.

B. ***Ornamental floriculture:*** It deals with the raising of flower crops for ornamental, pleasure and fashion purposes. *e.g.*: Dahlia, Zinnia, Cosmos, Hibiscus, Balsam, Nerium, Poinsettia, Hollyhock, Gerbera, and Gaillardia etc.

4. Landscape Gardening

It deals with the planning and execution of ornamental gardens, parks, landscape gardens etc.

5. Plantation Crops

Are those crops, which are cultivated in an extensive scale in large contiguous areas, owned and managed by an individual or a company and whose produce is utilized only after processing. *e.g.* Coffee, Tea, Rubber, Coconut, Cocoa etc.

6. Spices and Condiments

This branch deals with the cultivation of crops whose produce is used mainly for seasoning and flavouring dishes.

A. *Spices:* Are those plants the products of which are made use of as food adjuncts to add aroma and flavour. *e.g.* Pepper, Cardamom, Clove, Cinnamon, All spice, *etc.*

B. *Condiments:* Are those plants the products of which are made use of as food adjuncts to add taste only. *e.g.* Turmeric, Ginger, Red chillies, Onion, Garlic, *etc.*

7. Medicinal and Aromatic Plants

It deals with the cultivation of medicinal plants, which provide drugs and aromatic crops which yields aromatic (essential) oils.

A. *Medicinal plants:* Are those plants, which are rich in secondary metabolites and are potential sources of drugs. The secondary metabolites include alkaloids, glycosides, coumarins, flavonoides and steroids etc. *e.g.* Periwinkle, Opium, Menthi, Cinchona, Dioscorea Yam, Belladona, Senna, Sarpagandha, Aswagandha, Tulasi, *etc.*

B. *Aromatic plants:* Are those plants, which possesses essential oils in them. The essential oils are the odoriferous steam volatile constituents of aromatic plants. *e.g.* Lemon grass, Citronella, Palmrosa, Vetiver, Geranium, Davanam, Lavendor, *etc.*

Scope of Horticulture

There is a great scope of Horticulture. Horticulture production is less as compared and hence very high demand in market.

Present Status

Horticultural crops constitute a significant component of total agricultural production of the country.

Area and Production of Horticultural Crops as par NHB (2010-11)

Sl.No.	Crop		Area (000'ha)	Production (000 Mt.)
1.	Fruits	:	6383	74818
2.	Vegetables	:	8495	146554
3.	Flowers (Loose)	:	183 (2009-10)	1021 (2009-10)
4.	Aromatic and Medicinal crops	:	510	605
5.	Plantation crops	:	3306	12007
6.	Spices	:	2940	5350

1. **Increasing Investigation Facilities:** The agricultural sectors getting priority in the new five year plan outlay. There is definitely positive factor in keeping hope for bringing area under irrigation, Many irrigation projects, major and minor are in progress and many would be undertaken in near future. Number of percolation tanks is being constructed and new schemes.

2. **Area Under Rainfed:** Horticultural crops are not required the perennial irrigation.

3 **Transport and Marketing Facilities:** It is obvious that horticultural produce is perishable and mostly consumed as fresh and need quick disposal after harvest.

4. **Cold Storage Facilities and Preservation:** During peak period of a particular crop there is glut in market and prices realized are very low. This can be overcome by storing the fruits in cold storage. Many preserved products have export potential *e.g.* Jam, Jelly, Juices, Syrups etc.

5. **New Techniques for Maximization of Production:** This helps in increasing the yield.

    i) Use of Growth regulator increasing yield by 50 per cent in grapes.

    ii) Use of growth regulators.

6. **Availability of Cheap Labour:** In India because of large population man power is easily available and as compared to other countries the labour is cheap which definitely help in keeping down the production cost.

7. **Loan Facilities:** Many Commercial Banks and Government provide loans at low interest for the promotion of Horticultural Industry.

8. **Sloppy, undulated land can be brought under cultivation** by growing rain fed horticultural crops.

9. **The average production of the Horticultural crops is more than the agronomic crops** and therefore, the net returns are also more.

(B) Planting Methods

Systems/Methods of Orchard Planting

The arrangement of plants in the orchard is known as lay-out. The following points need to be considered before choosing a system of planting.

1. It should accommodate maximum number of plants per unit area.

2. It should allow sufficient space for the development of each tree.

3. It enables equal distribution of area under each tree.

4. The intercultural operations such as ploughing, spraying etc are easily carried out.

5. It makes supervision more easy and effective.

Methods/Systems of Planting Fruit Crops

1.
    Square system
2. Rectangular system
3. Triangular system
4. Hexagonal system
5. Quincunx system
6. Contour system

1. Square System

a. This is simplest system of fruit planting.

b. The plot is divided into square. A tree is planted at each corner of square.

c. In this system, intercultural operations can be done in both the direction as trees are at equal distance (row´tree).

d. This system of planting also facilitates for taking intercrops.

e. The major disadvantage of this system is that a lot of space in the centre of each square is wasted

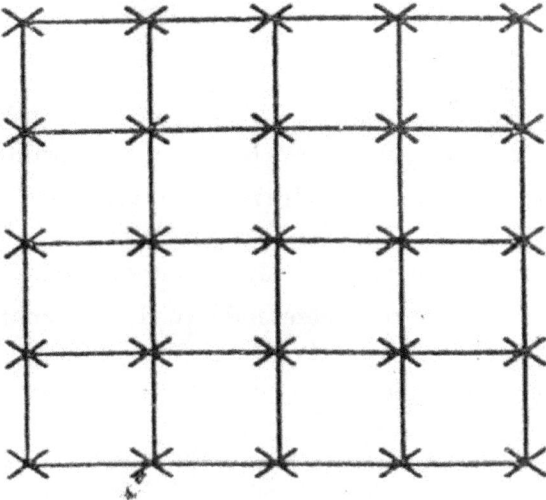

Square System

2. Rectangular System

a. In this system of planting, plot is divided into rectangle.

b. The trees are planted at 4 corners of the rectangle in straight rows running at right angles.

c. Rectangle system allows plants for planting in row with keeping more space.

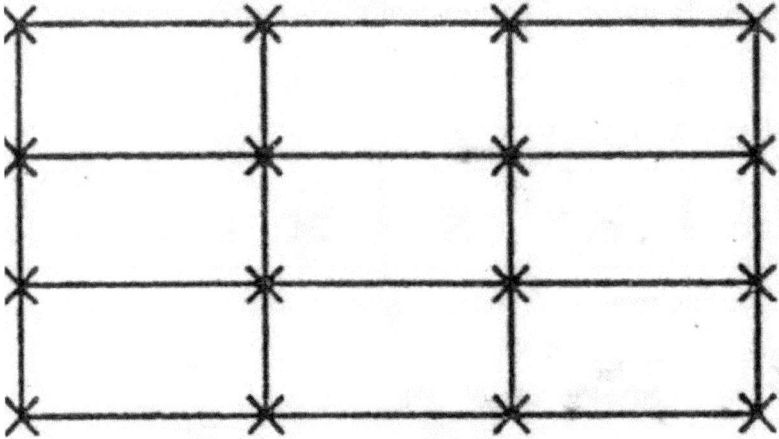

Rectangular System

3. **Triangle System**
    a. In this system of planting, a tree is planted on a corner of each angle.
    b. This has not much advantage over square system except it provides more open space to tree but intercultural operations are not easy to carry.

4. **Hexagonal System**
    a. Similar to square system, except that the distance between plants in the row and distance between rows is not the same but different.
    b. In this system of planting, a tree is planted at each corner of an equilateral triangle.
    c. In this way, six trees form a hexagon with seventh tree in the centre.
    d. The system is preferred where land is costly and very fertile with assured irrigation.
    e. 15 per cent more trees can be planted in hexagonal system than square system.

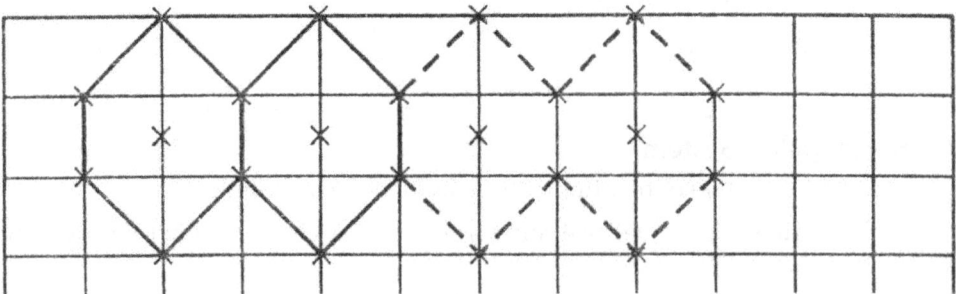

Hexagonal System

5. Quincunx System

a. This is also known as filler or diagonal system.

b. It is modified form of square system.

c. In this system, one tree is planted in the centre of the square of permanent trees. This tree is short lived and known as *'filler'* trees like banana, papaya, pomegranate, fig etc.

d. The filler trees are removed when main trees developed full canopy of start bearing.

e. This system is followed when the distance between permanent trees exceeds 8m or more or where permanent trees are very slow in their growth and also take longer time for coming to bearing. *e.g.* Sapota, Jackfruit.

f. This is economic to plant filler trees as they provide additional income to cultivators in the earlier years of the orchards.

g. The main advantage of this system is that the plant population is about double than the square system.

h. The greatest disadvantage of this system is that, it is difficult to carry out intercultural operations on account of the filler tree.

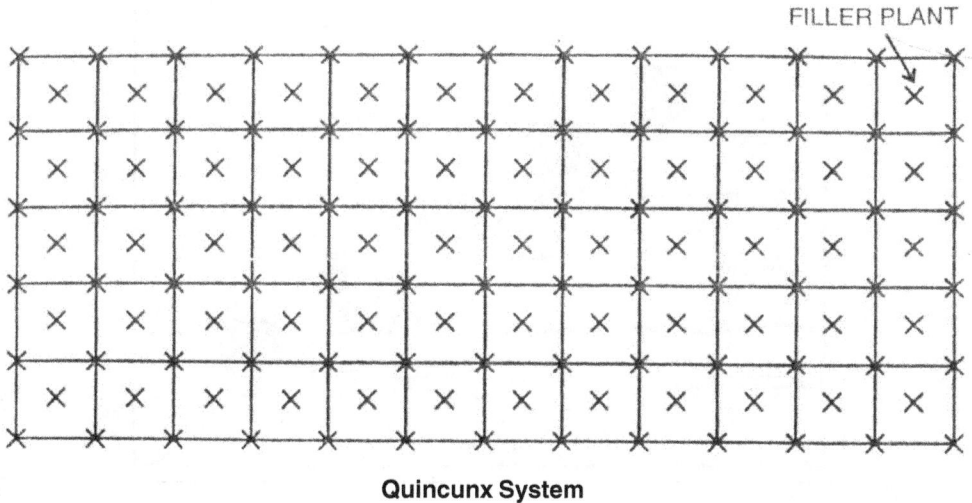

Quincunx System

6. Contour System

a. This is adopted in hilly areas for planting fruit plants, where land is undulated and soils erosion is a greater threat.

b. Under such circumstances, contour terrace is developed by scratching and levelling the hill slope.

c. The width of contour terrace varies according to the slope of the hill.

d. At stiff hill slope, the width is kept narrower.

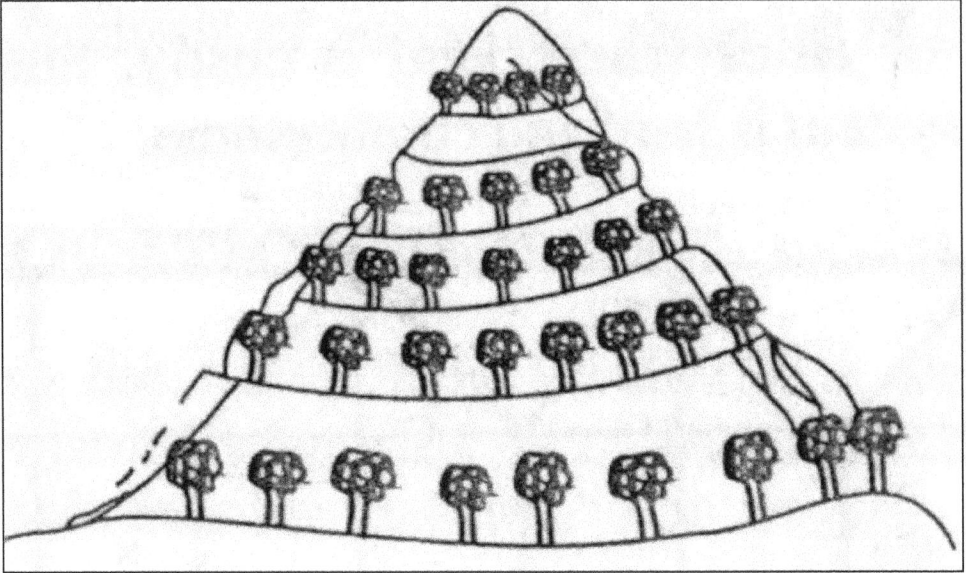

Contour System

(C) Nursery Raising Techniques

Following techniques/practices should be done to raise a good nursery for transplanting horticultural crops *i.e.* vegetables (especially for tomato, brinjal, cole crops etc.):

1. The nursery soil is preferred to fine tilth.

2. Raised beds are prepared to a height of 10-15 cm and an area of 60–80 sq. m nursery is sufficient for one acre.

3. Well decomposed FYM is mixed in the soil @ 3 kg FYM per m² of nursery bed.

4. A fertilizer dose of 0.5 kg N, P, K per bed is also mixed in the soil.

5. Seeds are treated with fungicides and 40 per cent formalin solution at 500 ml/m² area of nursery bed sterilisation. 10 per cent formaldehyde is also used for fumigation.

6. After fumigation the beds are covered with polythene for 24 hours.

7. Seeds are sown 4 to 5 days after removal of polythene sheets. In line sowing, 7.5 cm distance is kept between the rows.

8. Beds are covered with organic manures with increase in temperature promotes early germination, water is sprinkled.

9. The beds are covered with straw or polythene till the seeds germinate.

10. Seedlings are protected against wind, exposure to sun and excess rainfall. Fungicides are sprayed weekly to avoid of damping off.

11. Nursery can also be grown in poly house.

12. The seedlings should be hardened before setting them into field.

(D) Propagation Methods

Definition

Plant propagation can be defined as controlled reproduction of a plant by a man in order to perpetuate a selected individuals, or group of individuals which is having specific values to him.

There are two Method of Propagation:

1. Sexual Propagation
2. Asexual/Vegetative Propagation

1. Sexual Propagation in Plants

Multiplication of plants by using seed is called as sexual propagation. Asexual propagation or vegetative propagation refers to the multiplication or perpetuation of any plant from any vegetative parts as plant other then the seed.

Advantages of Vegetative Propagation

a. The progenies are true to type like mother plant.

b. Vegetative propagation is the only alternate where no seed is formed or germination of seed is very slow or no viable seed is formed. (*e.g.* Banana, Pine apple and roses, seedless grape).

c. Certain rootstock has the capacity of resisting or tolerating the adverse environment factors such as frost and adverse soil factors like salinity or alkalinity.

d. The ability of certain rootstock to resistant pest and diseases can be advantageously expected.

e. Vegetative propagated plants are generally dwarfed in nature than the seedlings. Dwarf trees facilitate pruning spraying and harvesting easy seedling.

f. To replant an undesirable existing tree either with reference to its quality or susceptibility to pests and diseases. The defect can be overcome easily by vegetative propagation through grafting or budding of desirable scion to the existence tree by top working technique.

g. Many plants are propagated by vegetative means because of the speedy easy of multiplication.

h. Novelty can be developed by grafting or budding on single plant many varieties. *e.g.* Roses.

i. To convert inferior varieties in superior, side grafting in mango.

Disadvantages

a. Plant is not vigorous and long lived.

b. No new varieties are evolved or developed.

c. These methods are expensive and laborious and time consuming.

2. Asexual/Vegetative Plant Propagations

A. Propagation by Cutting

B. Propagation by Layering

C. Propagation by Grafting

D. Propagation by Budding

E. Propagation by Special structures

A. Propagation by Cutting

"Cutting is a method of asexual propagation in which a portion of any vegetative part such as stem, leaf or root is cut from the parent plant and is placed under favorable environmental condition to form roots and shoots, thus producing a new independent plant."

a) Stem Cutting

This is the most important type of cutting and can be divided into three types based on the nature of the wood used in marketing the cutting.

i) Hard wood cutting

ii) Semi-hard wood cutting

iii) Soft-wood cutting.

i) **Hard Wood Cuttings:** This is last expensive and easiest method. The cutting usually prepared during the dormant season and from the wood of the previous season growth. Hard wood cuttings are not readily perishable and may be shifted safely over long distance, if necessary. *e.g.* Grape, pomegranate, fig, mulberry, Acalypa, Rose etc

ii) **Semi-hard Wood Cuttings:** The cuttings are prepared from now shoot just after a flush of growth which is partially matured. *e.g.* Exanthema.

iii) **Soft-wood Cutting:** These types of cuttings are also made from succulent, herbaceous green plants such as carnation, portulaces, etc. These cuttings are always made with leaves attached to stem. *e.g.* Coleus, pilea, alternanthea, etc.

b) Leaf Cuttings

In these type cuttings, the leaf blade, sometimes with petiole, is utilized in starting a new plant. In most cases adventitious roots and an adventitious shoot develop at the leaf base. *e.g.* snake plant, Begonia rex, blackberry, camellia.

c) Root Cuttings

In preparing root cuttings the period when the plant is in rapid growth must be avoided. It is important to maintain the correct polarity when planting the root cuttings. *e.g.* Guava, Pahadi gulab, India cork tree.

B. Propagation by Layering

Layering is the development of roots on a stem while it is still attached to the parent plant. The rooted stem is stem is then detached to become a new plant growing on its own roots. Thus rooted stem is known as layer.

a) Simple Layering or Tongue Layering

In this method a branch is bent to the ground and some portion of it, is covered by soil leaving the terminal and of the branch exposed. Root initiation takes place at the buried portion. After the root initiation. *i.e.* after allowing sufficient time the layer is separated from the mother plant by cutting the layered shoot. *e.g.* Guava, jasmine, etc.

b) Compound or Serpentine Layering

Compound layering in essentially the same as simple layering. Except that the branch is alternatively covered and exposed along length. The branch for compound layering must be longer one, so that is can be layered at different place and to branch. This method can be longer one, so that it can be layered at different place and to branch. This method can be followed easily for creepers. *e.g.* Guava.

c) Mound Layering or Stooling

In this method a plant is cut back at the ground during the dormant season, and soil is covered at the base of the newly developing shoots. After allowing sufficient time for root initiation, the rooted shoots are separated and taken as individual layers.

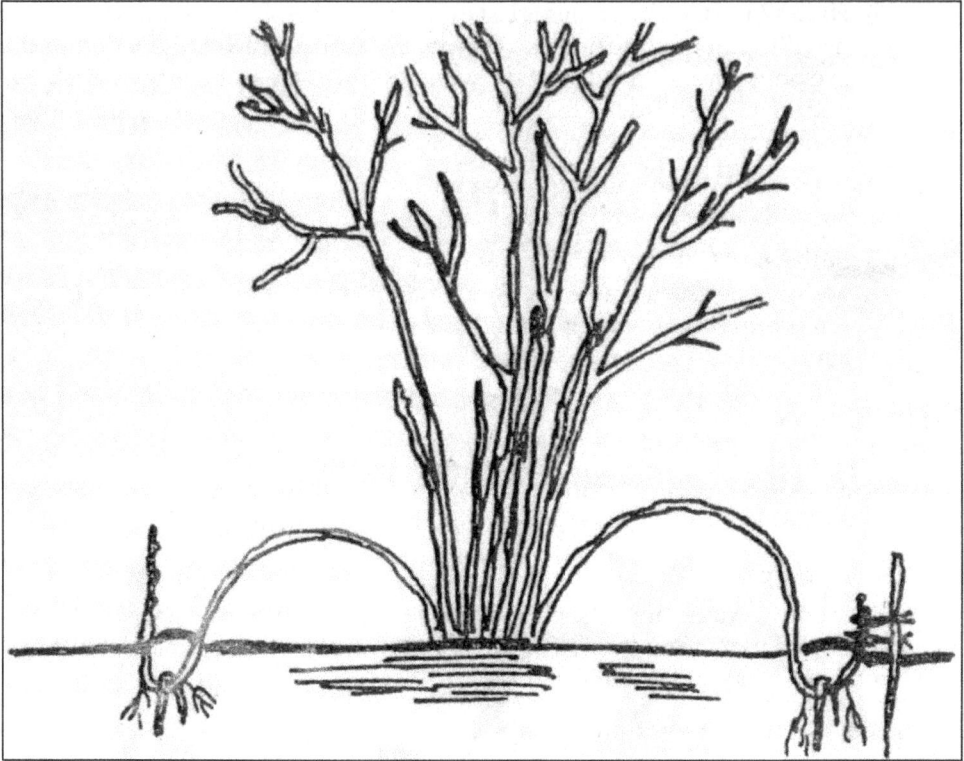

Simple Layering

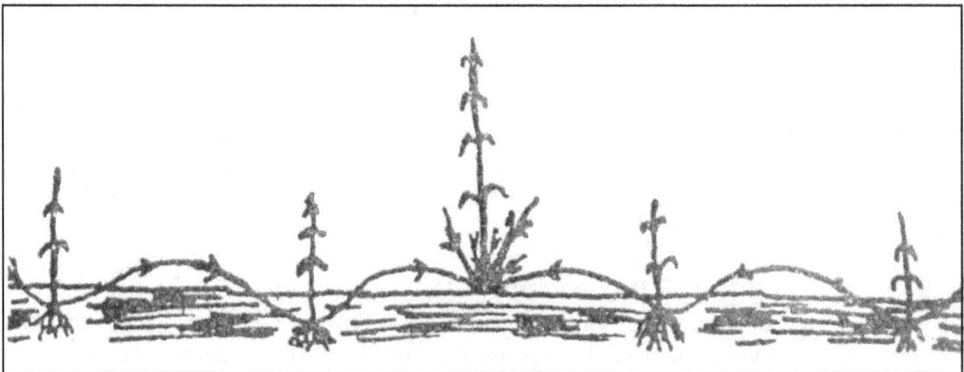

Compound/Spending Layering

d) Air Layering or Gootee

In air layering, roots appears on an aerial shoots. The rooting medium will be tied to the shoots for getting root initiation. Best rooting medium for air layering is sphagnum- moss as it holds large amounts of water so as to supply moisture to the layered shoot till proper root initiation takes place. *e.g.* Pomegranate.

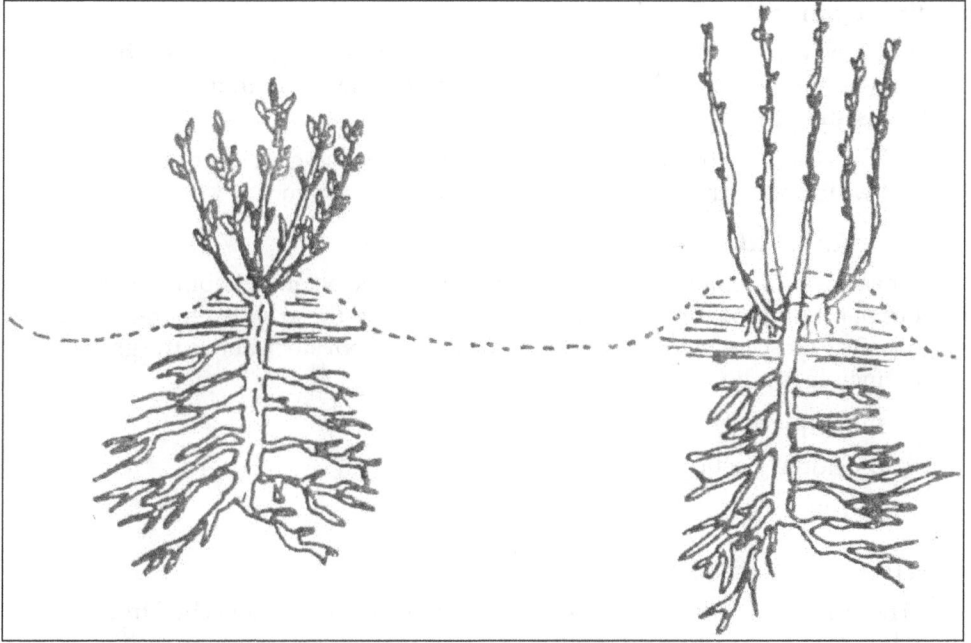

Mound Layering/Stooling

Air Layering/Marcotage/Gootee

C. Propagation by Grafting

Grafting is an art of joining two different plant parts together, in such a manner that they unites and continues their growth as simple plant. In this method, a bud stick consisting two or more buds is inserted in to the stock.

Stock is a lower portion of the graft union, where as, scion is the upper portion a place at which both unites is termed as scion or graft union.

a) Scion Attached Methods

These are the methods of grafting where in the scion is kept attached to the mother plant till the graft union takes place and then the graft is separated in stage taking cuts   on scion below the graft union and on root stock above the graft union. This principle is followed in following methods:

   i) Simple approach or inarching.

   ii) Saddle grafting.

   iii) Tongue grafting.

b) Scion Detached Methods

These are the grafting methods where in the scion is first detached from mother plan then inserted in to root stock so as the union takes place and combination continues to grow. These methods are:

   i) Veneer grafting.

   ii) Wedge grafting.

   iii) Saddle grafting.

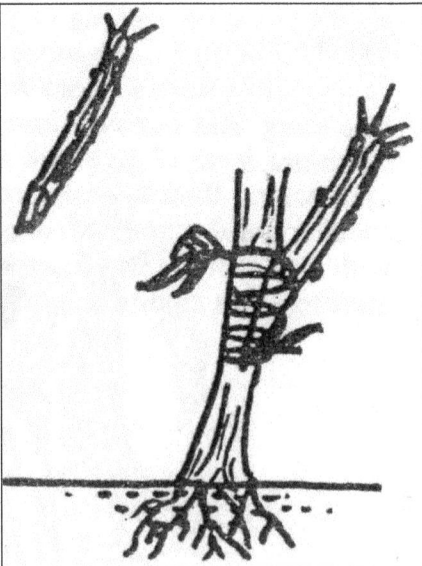

Veneer Grafting

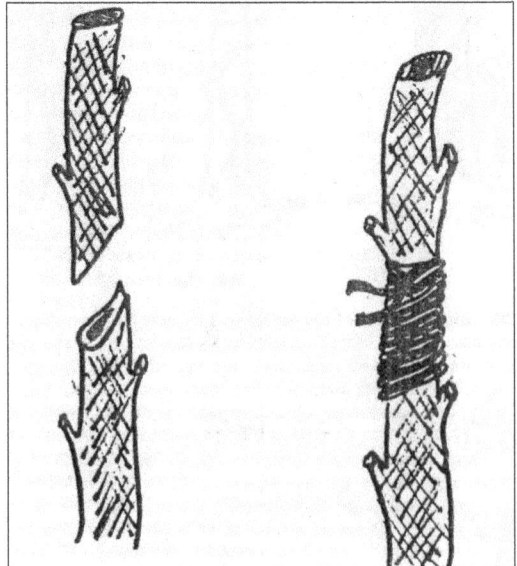

Whip Grafting

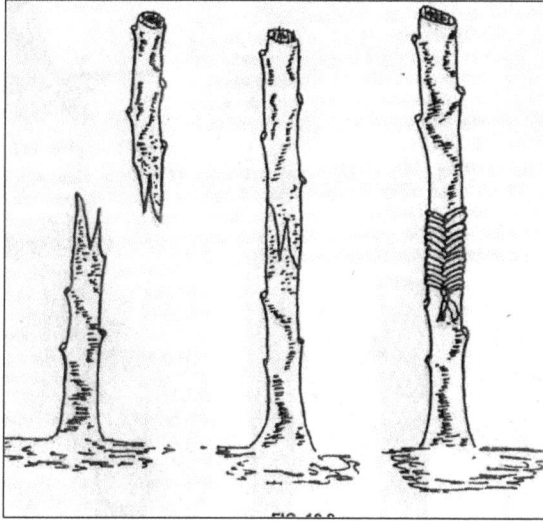

Tongue Grafting

Cleft Grafting

Bridge Grafting

iv) Whip and tongue grafting.

v) Whip grafting.

vi) Stone grafting.

vii) Softwood grafting.

c) Methods of Grafting on Established Trees

Methods which can be successfully adopted to convert the inferior established plants in to the superior or desired one. These are

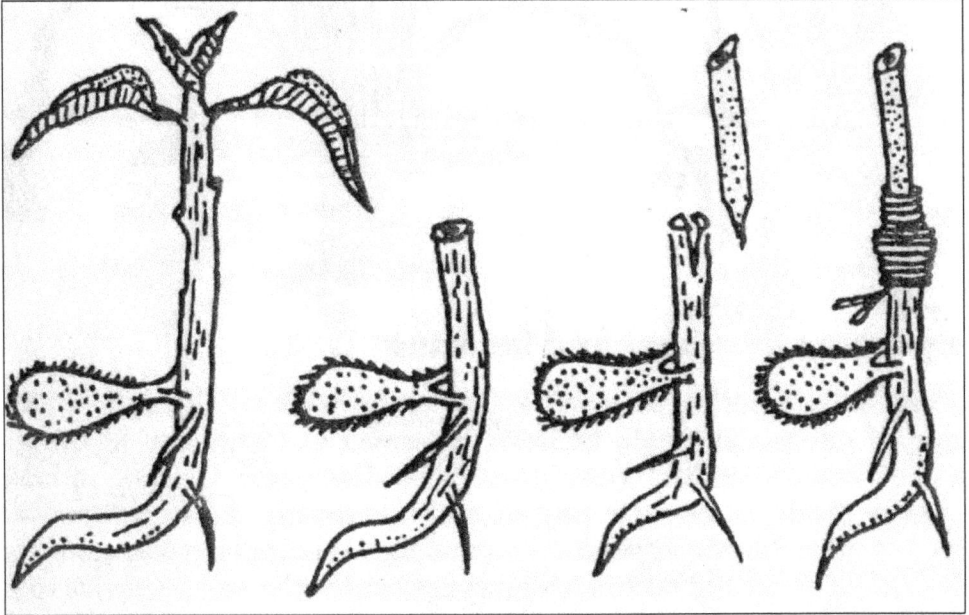

Epicotyl Grafting

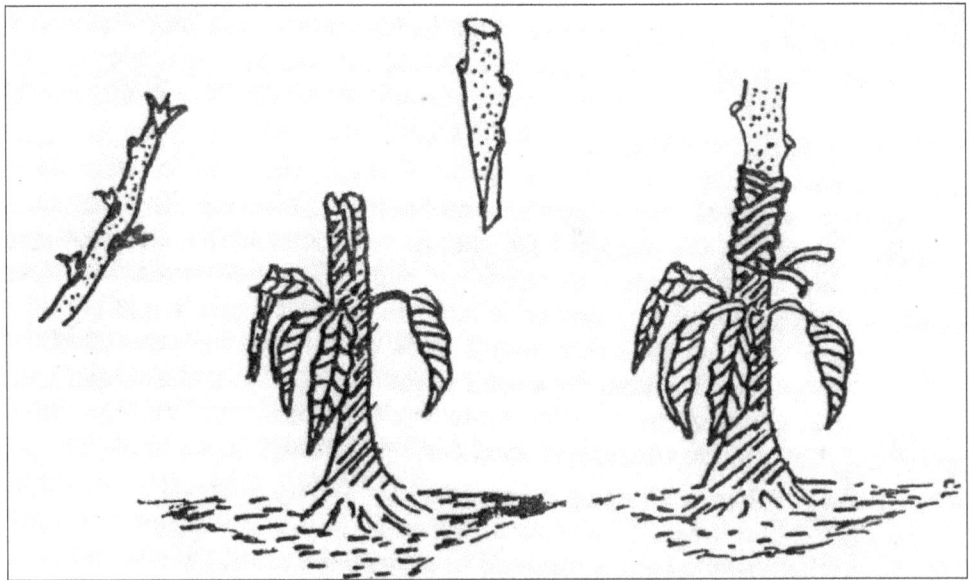

Softwood Grafting

i) Side grafting

ii) Crown grafting

iii) Top working.

Inarching

D. Propagation by Budding

Budding is the vegetative method of plant propagation and can be defined as an art of insertion of a single mature bud in to the stem of the rootstock in such way that the union takes place and the combination continues to grow. It is grafting of a single individual bud instead of whole bud stick on scion as in done in case of grafting.

Different Techniques of Methods of Budding are as follows:

a) Shield Budding

This is the methods of budding in which a single bud with a little wood or without wood is taken but from the scion plant and is given a shape of 'shield' before it is inserted into the root stock. It is done in following ways:

   i) Selection of Bud Wood or Bud Stock

   ii) Selection of Stock Plant

   iii) Removal of Bark from the Stalk Plant

   iv) Removal of Bud

   v) Inserting the Bud

   vi) Bandaging

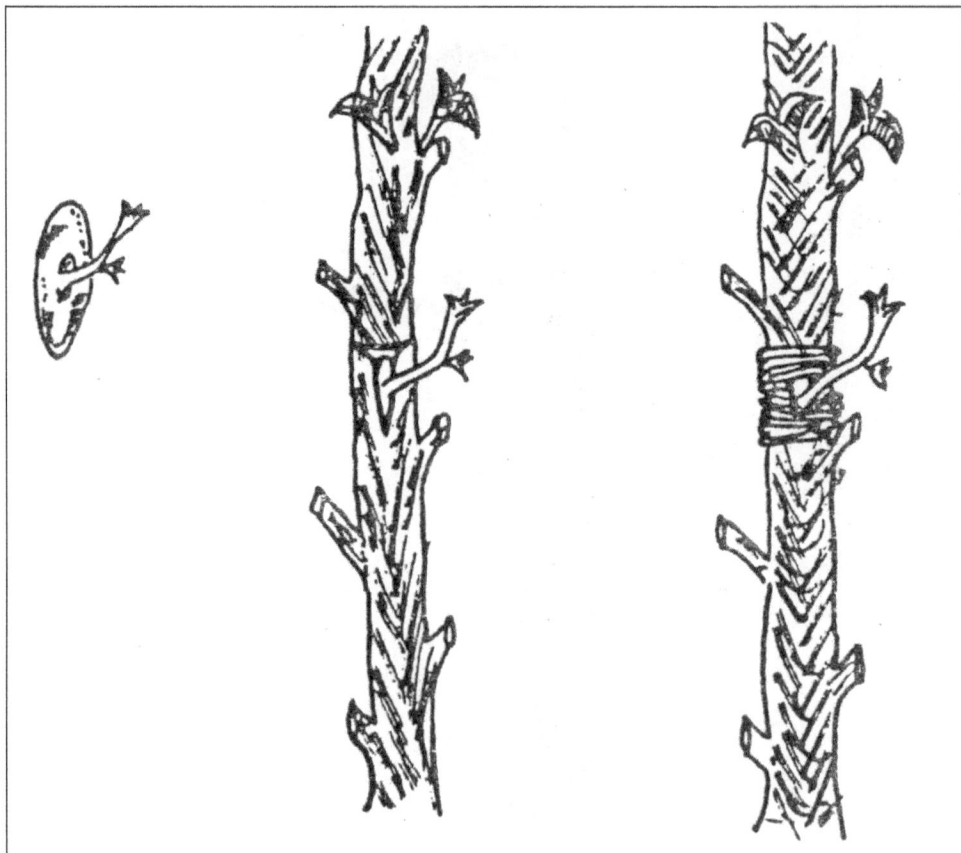

Shield Budding

b) Shield Budding by 'I' Method

It is adopted where a great deal of rains occur. Water running down the stem of the root stock. After in case of the 'T' cut soaks under the bud and causes decay of the shield piece of bud. Under such condition and 'inverted' T budding may give better results, since it is more likely to the below the bark inform running water.

The technique required in this method is same as that in T method except that the incision on the stock has the transceivers (cross) is taken on root stock and it is bent so that the bark become loose. Then the bud is inserted and tied firmly with sutali. Union takes place within two to three weeks.

c) Simple Shield Budding by Insertion Method

A simple length wise incision (cut) is taken on root stock and it is bent so that the bark becomes loose. Then the bud is inserted and tied firmly with sutali. Union takes place within two to three weeks.

I) **Patch Budding:** The patch of bark is removed from the stem of the root stock. Then the patch of bud of exactly the same size is removed from the bud stock taken from desired tree and fitted on the root stock exposed area. Polythene film is tied to protect same. Separating and October are considerable to rather most suitable months for patch budding in mango.

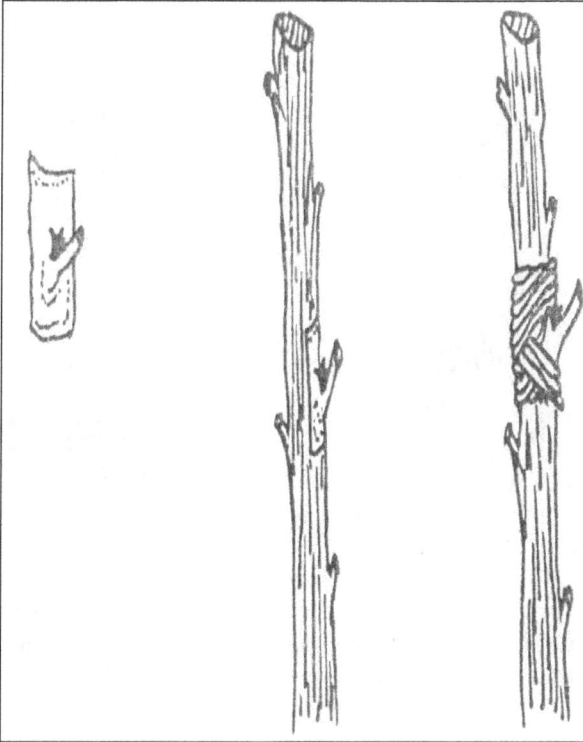

Patch Budding

II) **Flute Budding:** This method makes use of the ring of tissues adjoin the bud relatively thick barked tree thicker than 1 cm. and in active stage of are commonly budded by this method. It is successfully used in Ber and Cashewnunt trees.

III) **Ring Budding:** The nature and method rendered its usefulness only to small stocks of not more than ¾ to 1 diameter. This is more or less an extension of flute method. Budding operation is performed when the plant is in sap flowing condition. A complete (1 ½ to 2) ring of bark is removed around the stem of the stock in order to from matrix. A complete ring of bark of the same with a prominent, plumy, healthy bud is removed from bud stick when placed on stock; it extends all around the stock. After placing the ring in position typing is done in usual manner, failure of the bud to unite, result in loss of terminal portion of stock above the ringed portion.

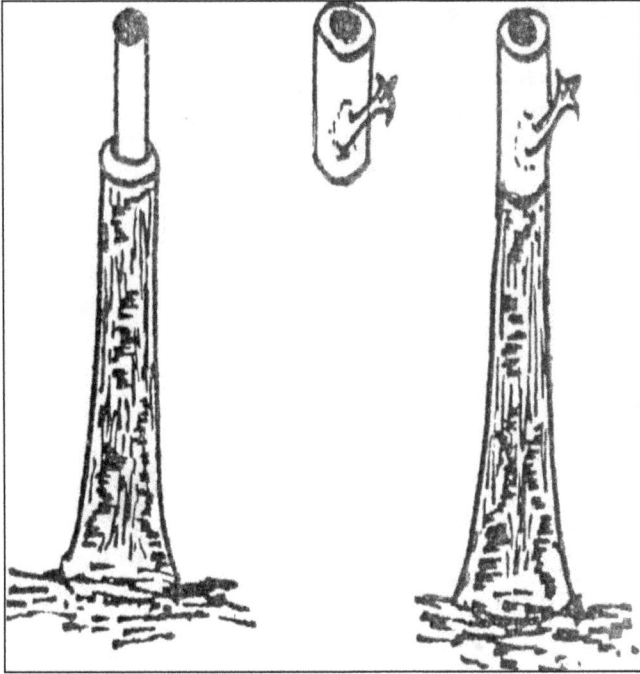

Ring Budding

IV) **Forkert Budding:** The selection of the bud sticks as well as the root stock is the same as that in the shield budding. At the height of about 9 to12 from the ground level horizontal cut is taken on the root stock and then two vertical cuts from the either end of the horizontal cut extending downwards

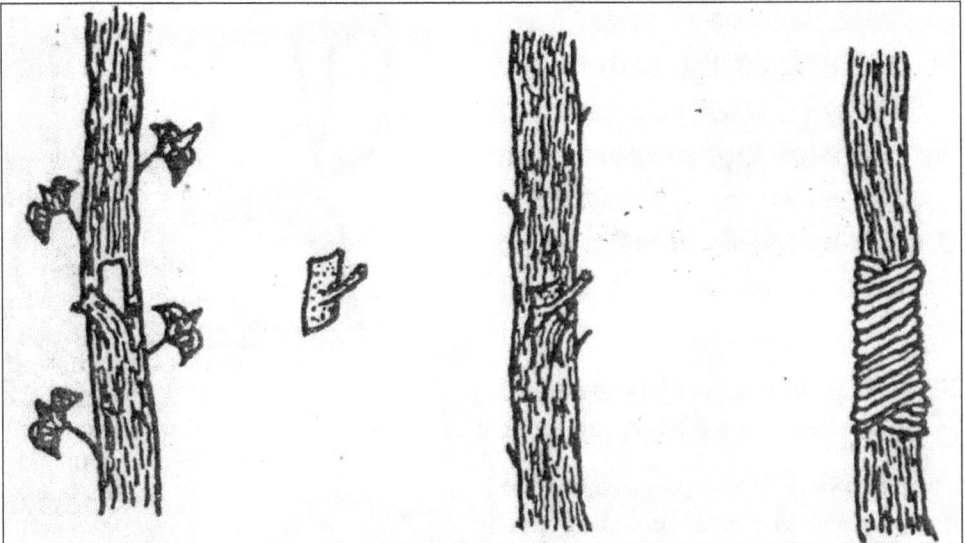

Forkert Budding

are taken and a flap of bark is pooled out exposing a rectangular portion of about 1 to 2 on the root stock. A rectangular piece of bark along with a matured primly bud, of the same size is removed from the selected bud stick. This piece of bark is then fitted on the exposed portion on root stock and secured well. The panel of bark is then released to its original position and tied by sutali is done in a usual way. The manuring, watering of the root stock is carried out as and when required.

After about 15 days the bandage is removed. The panel of bark is pooled out again and the inside is observed. If the bud shown the sign of sprouting, the panel of bark is removed by taking horizontal incision the downside of its on the root stock and the bud is again bandage, keeping exposed the growing point in a usual way. If the bud does not show the sign of sprouting the panel of bark is released to its original position and bandage is done in a usual way. After 15 days same procedure is followed.

Within 3 to 5 weeks from the operation the buds sprouts. When the shoot coming from the bud grows vigorously the terminal shoot of the root stock is removed or cut off in two to three steps as is done in the case of shield budding.

E. Propagation by Special Structures

a) Suckers

A sucker is a shot which arises on a plant from below the ground. The most precise use of this term is to designate a shoot which arises from an adventitious bud on root. The tendency to suckers is a characteristic possessed by some plants and not other. *e.g.* Banana, red raspberry, black berry and chrysanthemum.

b) Crows

The term crown is used to designate the part of a plant stem at and below the surface of the ground from which new shoots are produced. Division of the crown is an important method of propagation and this division wills plants. *e.g.* African violet, strawberry.

c) Bulb

Bulbs are produced by monocotyledons plants in which the usual structure is modified for storage and reproduction. A bulb is a specialized underground organ consisting a short, fleshy, unusually vertical stem axis, at apex a growing point and enclosed by thick flexi scales. Bulb scales morphologically are the continuous sheathing leaf bases. Bulbs will be separated and used for propagation. *e.g.* onion, bulbous iris.

d) Corms

A corm is the swollen base of a stem axis enclosed by the dry, scale like leables. (in contrast to the bulb) which is predominantly leaf scalds a corm is a solid stem structure with district nodes and internodes. Propagation is dry forms which will develop on the corm. *e.g.* Gladiolus.

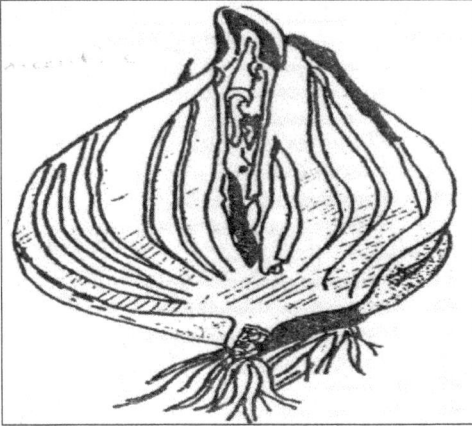

Bulb

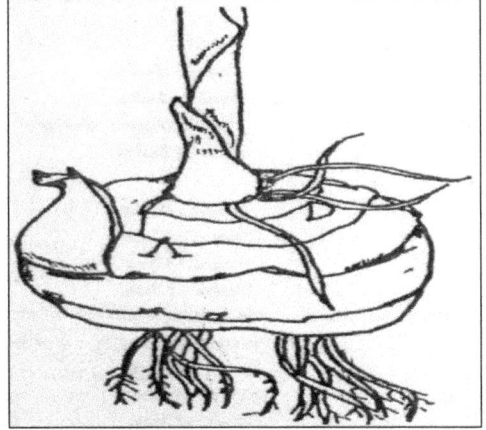

Corm

e) Tubers (Stem Tubers)

A stem tuber is the short terminal portion of an underground stem which has become thickened because of the accumulation of reserve food materials. *e.g.* potato, propagation by tuber can be carried out either by planting the whole tubers or by cutting them into sections, each containing a bud or eye.

f) Tuberous Roots (Root Tubers)

Certain herbaceous perennial produce thickened roots which contain large amount of stored food. The tuberous roots differ from the tubers in that they lack nodes and internodes. Adventitious buds are present only at stem and these fleshy roots are separated and used propagation. *e.g.* Sweet potato, Dahlia.

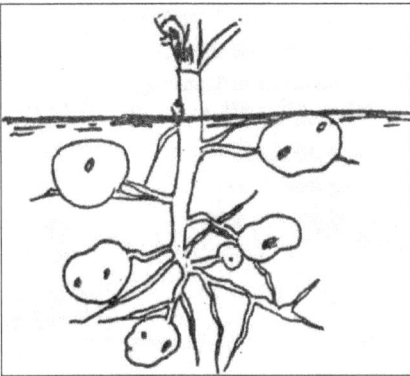

Tuber

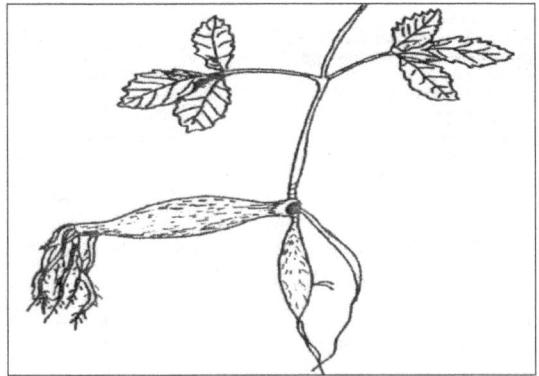

Tuberous Roots

g) Rhizomes

A rhizome is a horizontal stem growing either underground or along the surface of the ground. Typically it is the main axis of the plant, producing roots on it lower surface and extends leaves and flowering shoots above the ground. It may be thick

Rhizome

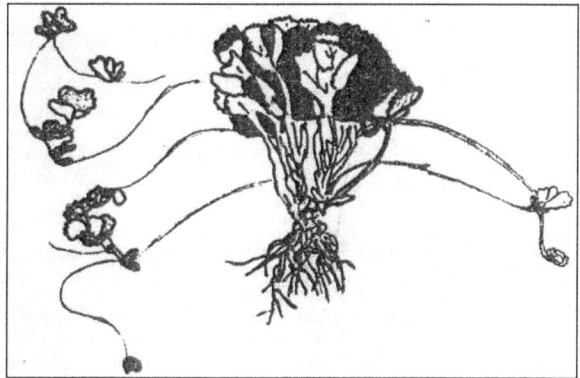

Runner

and fleshy or slender and elongated but it is always made up of nodes and inters nodes. *e.g.* Canna, Ginner, propagation by Rhizomes.

h) Runners

A runner is specialized stem which develops from the axial of a leaf at the crown of a plant. Grows horizontally along the ground and forms a new plant at one of the nodes. *e.g.* strawberry.

i) Stolen

Stolen is a term used to describe various types of horizontally growing stems that produce adventitious rots when comes in contact with the soil. Specifically these are prostrate stems as found in Bermuda grass (*Cynodon dactylon*), the underground stem of the potato that terminal as in tuber is a stolen.

Micro Propagation

Definition

Micro propagation (tissue culture or in-vitro culture) refers to the multiplication of plants, in aseptic condition and in artificial growth medium. From very small plant parts like Meristem tip, callus embryos, anther etc.

Merits of Micro Propagation

1. Tissue culture helps in rapid multiplication of true plats throughout the year.

2. A new plant can be regenerated from a miniature plant part, whereas in conventional methods a shoot of considerable length is required.

3. Large number of plants can be produced in culture tubes in small space with uniform growth and productivity of growing them in large area in nursery.

4. Plants raised by tissue culture are free from diseases.

5. Tissue culture coupled with somatic hybridization helps in evolving new cultivar in a short time.

6. Micro propagation facilitates long distance transport of propagation material and long term storage of clonal materials.

7. Tissue culture methods are not viable (male sterile) or not available easily (*e.g.* banana) and in plant where propagation by conventional methods are expensive (*e.g.* orchid).

Demerits of Micro Propagation

1. The cost involved in setting up and maintenance of laboratory is very high and may not justify their use in all the horticultural plants ordinarily.

2. Tissue culture techniques require skill and manpower.

3. Slight infection may damage the entire lot of plants.

4. Some genetic modification (mutation) of the plant may develop with some varieties and culture systems which may alter the quality of the produce.

5. The seedling grown under artificial condition may not survive when placed under environmental condition directly if thing is not given.

Methods of Micro-Propagation

(A) Meristem Culture

In Meristem culture the Meristem and a few subtending leaf primordial are placed into a suitable growing media. Art elongated rooted platelet is produced after some weeks is transferred to soil when it has attained a considerable height. A disease free plant can be produced by this method. Experimental results also suggest that this technique can be successfully utilized for rapid multiplication of various herbaceous plants.

(B) Callus Culture

A callus is mass of undifferentiated parenchymatus cells. When a living plant tissue is placed in an artificial growing medium with other conditions favourable, callus is formed. The growth of callus varies with the homogenous levels of Auxin and Cytokinin and can be manipulated by endogenous supply of these growth regulators in the culture medium.

(C) Embryo Culture

In embryo culture, the embryo is excised and placed into a culture medium with proper nutrient in aseptic condition. To obtain a quick and optimum growth has growth into a platelets, it is transferred to soil. It is particularly important for the production of interspecific and intergeneric hybrids and to overcome the embryo abortion.

Protoplast Culture

In embryo culture, the plant cell can be isolated with the help of wall degrading enzymes and growth in a suitable culture medium in a controlled condition for regeneration of plantlets. Under suitable condition suitable condition the protoplast develop a cell wall followed by an increase in cell division and differention and grow into a new plant. The protoplast are fist culture in liquid medium at 25 to 28 C with a light intensity of 100 to 500 lux or in dark and after undergoing substantial cell division, they are transferred into solid medium congenial or morphogenesis in many horticultural crops response well to protoplast culture.

(E) Training and Pruning

☆ Training and pruning are important operations. Both the operations form an indispensable process having direct bearing on growth and vigour of plants and yield and quality of fruits.

☆ A properly trained and pruned plant sustain heavy crop load and produce bounteous harvest of quality.

☆ **Training** is a treatment given to the young plants to get a suitable or desirable shape with strong framework. It may or may not involve pruning. **Pruning** is the removal of unwanted, surplus annual growth; dead, dried and diseased wood of the plants is called Pruning.

☆ Both the operations of training and pruning work together in maintaining shape and size of tree and harvesting desirable yield.

Training

☆ When the plant is stalked or tied or supported over a trellis or pergola in certain fashion or some of its parts are removed or trimmed with a view to give the plant a particular shape, this operation is called training.

☆ Training controls the shape of plant.

☆ It aims at proper distribution of fruit bearing parts, control of insects and diseases, checking loss from breakage and determines the proper grade or quality of fruit.

Principles of Training

The system of training followed the general principles are:

1. The branches should arise on the main trunk alternatively at intervals of at least 15cm and not all at one place.

2. They should be equally distributed around the stem.

3. Up right branches should not be encouraged. Branches should have medium crotches.

Types of Training System

    (A) Centre leader system

    (B) Open centre system

    (C) Modified leader system

(A) Centre Leader/Pyramid System

1. The main trunk is allowed to develop without interruption. The first branch is allowed to grow at 45 to 50 cm height from ground level and other branches are allowed to grow on main stem at a distance of 15 to 20 cm.

2. This system is also called as **close centre**, since the centre of the plant is closed and also as **pyramidal** system, since the plant trained looks like a pyramid.

3. This system of training is practiced in case of certain apple varieties and pears.

4. Difficult to spray, prune, thin and harvest.

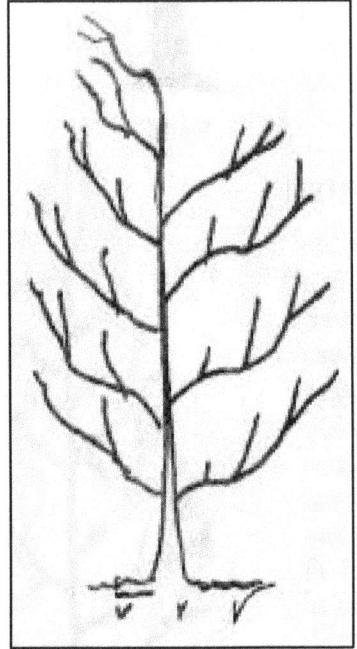

Central Leader System

(B) Open Centre/Open Head System

1. The main trunk is beheaded, when the plant attains a height of 40 to 50 cm. 3-5 nearly equally developed primary lateral branches which are well scattered, arranged and distributed are allowed to develop from trunk.

2. This system leads to a spreading structure, through with somewhat weaker crotches facilitating thinning, spraying, picking, removal of diseased portions.

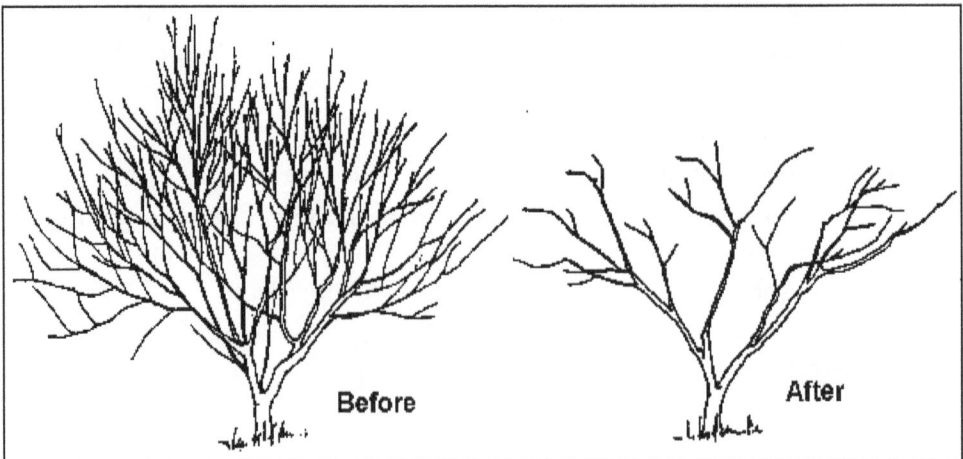

Before

After

Open Centre System

3. It exposes the tree to maximum extent and this has a uniform distribution of fruits on the branches.

4. This system is not suitable for high altitude where frost observance is common.

5. It is mostly practised in peaches, apple cherries and American type of plum.

(C) Modified Leader System

1. This is intermediate form of central leader and open centre system and draws the benefits of both systems.

2. It is first trained like centre leader by allowing stem to grow for first 4-5 years and then headed back to 75-120 cm height from ground level.

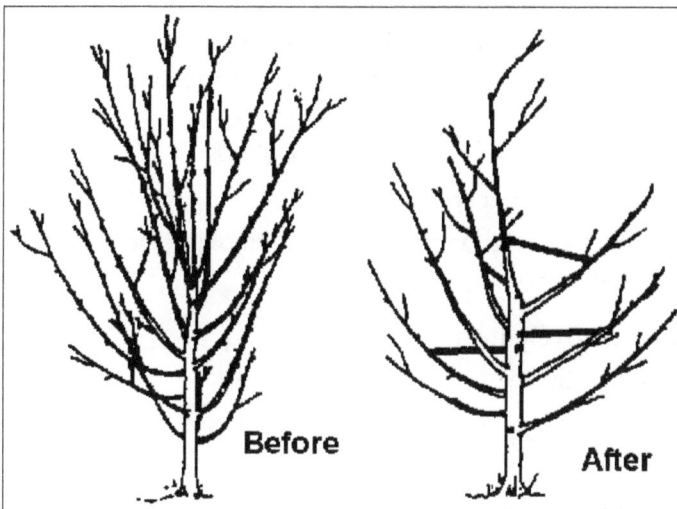

Modified Leader System

3. On the main stem, the first shoot is selected at the height of 40 cm from the ground and 4 to 5 branches located at a distance of 15 to 20 cm and placed all around the main stem are selected.

4. When properly formed, it provides stronger crotches, better spacing between laterals and more height than open head tree.

5. Easy in spraying, pruning and harvesting.

6. This system of training is practiced in fruit plants like citrus, pear, apple and walnut etc.

Pruning

☆ Removal of any excess or undesirable/unproductive branches, shoots or any other parts of plants so as to allow the remaining part to grow normally or according to desire of prunner is called pruning.

☆ It improves the shape of plant, influences the growth behaviour, flowering time and fruitfulness, besides improving the quality of fruit.

Objectives of Pruning

1. To remove the surplus branches and direct the sap flow in to the remaining branches.

2. To develop a strong frame work which can carry the load of a good crop and can with stand strong winds.

3. To train the plants to a definite shape. *e.g.* Fence, Hedge, Topiary etc.

4. To thin out branches so as to admit more light into the interior of the tree top so that the inner wood also becomes fruitful.

5. To limit the size of the tree top to a convenient one so as to render spraying and picking more easy and economically.

6. To regulate the spacing and distribution/direction of branches.

7. To distribute the fruiting wood in all directions and to maintain a balance between vegetative and reproductive phases.

8. To check the further spread of the diseases.

9. To maintain the vigour of the plant by removing the water shoots and other unwanted growth.

Types of Pruning System

(A) Heading back

(B) Thinning out

(C) Ringing

(D) Notching

(A) Heading Back

1. When the branches grow tall and vigorously without producing flowers, these shoots are headed back. When a branch is cut almost to the base, leaving a few inches of stump, carrying few buds, it is referred as Heading Back.

2. These buds left on the stump will give rise to shoots which are important to the tree either being spur bearers or bearing flower buds or filling up of gaps in the tree or forming vegetative wood from which flowers may arise in the following year. The shoot from the bud nearest to the cut takes the place of the pruned shoot.

3. It stimulates the development of more growing points than corresponding thinning out.

(B) Thinning Out

1. When a shoot is removed entirely from the inception (from the point of origin) so that, no new shoot arises from that place, it is referred as thinning out. This thinning is practiced in the removal of shoots arising in unwanted places, water shoots etc.

(C) Ringing/Girdling

1. In this process, a circular ring of bark measuring about 3 cm in length is removed.

(D) Notching

1. Making a notch above a bud by removing a wedge shaped piece of bark is termed as notching.

2. It checks the influence of hormone and encourages growth.

(E) Pollarding

1. Cutting back of the shoots, indiscriminately to reduce the height of the tree is Pollarding.

(F) Pinching (Tipping)

1. Removal of the tip of the shoot to stop its indeterminate growth or to encourage the growth of the lateral buds is pinching or tipping.

2. This is practiced in marigold and chillies at the time of transplanting.

(G) Disbudding (nipping or rubbing)

1. Nipping or rubbing of young buds preventing a chance of their sprouting is disbudding. When the buds arise in wrong places they are rubbed off. Similarly sprouts (Buds) on root stocks are disbudded.

(H) De-blossoming

1. Removal of surplus flowers to enable the tree to produce crops regularly year after year is called deblossoming.

2. This is practiced in alternate bearers like mango, apple etc.

(F) Irrigation Methods and Fertigation

Irrigation

☆ Irrigation is the artificial application of water to the soil to supplement the rainfall and groundwater contribution to assist the crop production.

☆ Irrigation is the artificial application of water for the purpose of supplying moisture essential to plant growth.

Objectives/Importance of Irrigation

1. To supply the moisture essential for plant growth.

2. For better utilization of production factors (nutrients).

3. To provide crop insurance against short spells of drought.
4. To dilute/washout soluble salts
5. To soften tillage pans
6. Intensive cropping is made possible
7. Timely seedbed preparation and timely sowing.
8. To create favourable microclimate for crop growth.
9. Higher yields as well as stability in production

Methods of Irrigation

(A) Surface irrigation method
(B) Sub surface irrigation method
(C) Micro irrigation methods

(A) Surface Irrigation Method

1. Flooding
2. Check-basin
3. Ring-basin
4. Border strip
5. Furrow method
6. Surge method

1. Flooding

i) Used for lowland rice and other crops.
ii) Water is allowed from the channel into the field without much control on either sides of the flow.

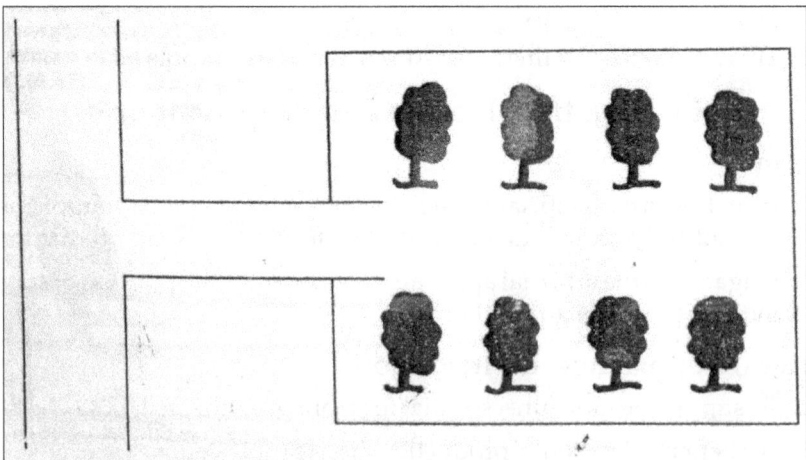

Flooding System

   iii) It covers the entire field and move almost unguided.

   iv) The height of bunds around the field should be 15 cm for effective use of rainfall.

   v) It is a minimum labour intensive method.

Advantages

   i) Less labour required,

   ii) No extra care,

   iii) Large stream can be easily managed.

Disadvantages

   i) Uneven distribution of water,

   ii) Low water application efficiency.

2. Check-basin

   i) Most common method of surface irrigation.

   ii) The field is divided into small plots surrounding by small bunds on all four sides.

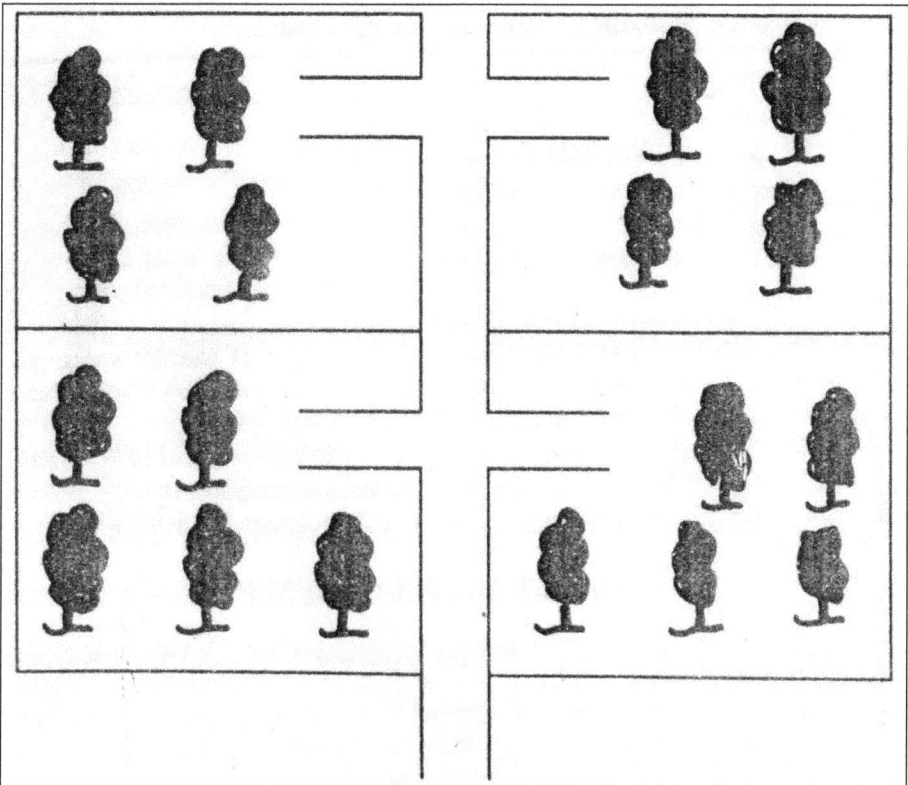

Check-Basin System

iii) Water from head channel is supplied to the field channel one after another.

iv) Each field channel supplied water to 2 row of check basin and water is applied to one basin after another.

v) The size of check basin ranges from 4 m x 3 m to 6 m x 5 m depending upon stream size and soil texture.

Advantages

i) Uniformily water application,

ii) Suitable for those fields which are quite large and not easy to level the entire field.

Disadvantages

i) More labour required for field layout and irrigation

ii) Wastage of field/land is more under irrigations and bunds. Mostly 5 per cent of land is waste for bunding.

3. Ring-basin Method

i) Basins around the trees are made.

ii) It is suitable for fruit trees.

iii) It enhances the water use efficiency and fewer losses.

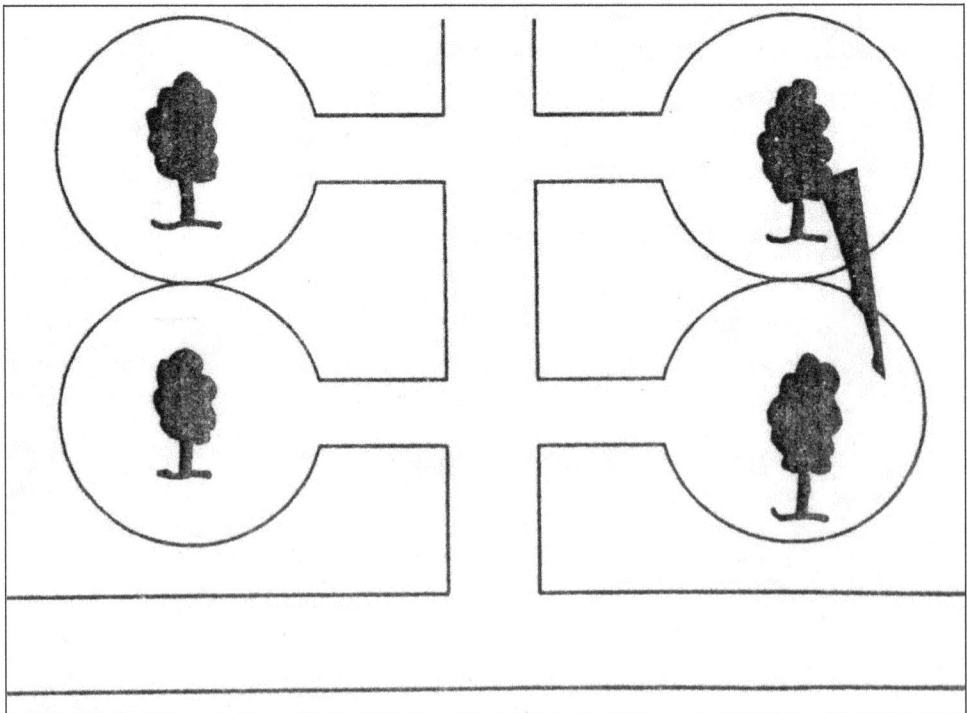

Ring-Basin System

iv) Basins are generally round in shape and occasionally square shaped.

v) Basins are small when the fields are young and the size is increased with age of trees.

vi) Basins are connected by channel irrigation.

4. Border Strip Method

i) Field divided into number of strips by bunds of around 15 cm height,

ii) These parallel earth ridges (called border) are formed to guide the flow of the water across the field,

iii) Length of strip ranges from 30m – 50m, while width is from 3m - 5m,

iv) The slope ranges from 0.1-1 per cent,

v) Water from the channel is allowed into each strip at a time,

vi) This method is suitable for close growing crops and medium to heavy texture soils, but not suitable for sandy soils.

Advantages

i) Large irrigation streams can be efficiently used,

ii) This method gives highest water use efficiency than other surface irrigation methods.

Disadvantages

i) No uniform distribution of water,

ii) This method can not applied for sandy soil.

5. Furrow Method

i) Furrows are formed along or across the slope and water from pipes is diverted into the furrows.

ii) Water infiltrate from the bottom and sides of the furrow moving downward and laterally to wet the soil.

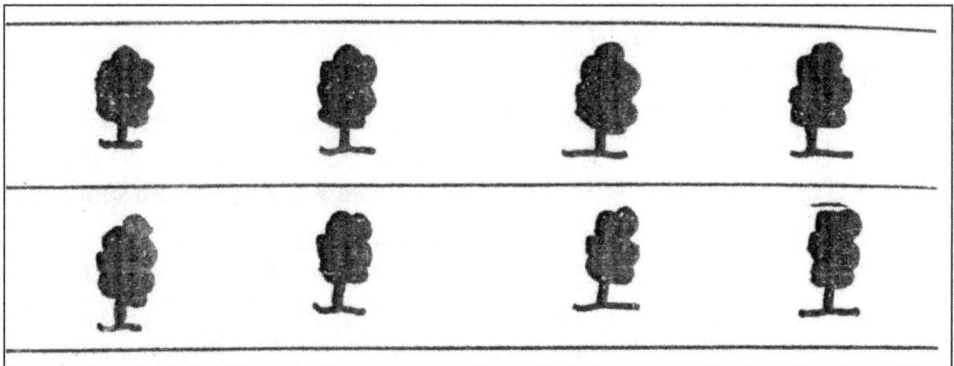

Furrow System

      iii) Water is allowed into 3-5 furrows at a time from open ditches and or pipes.

      iv) This method is adapted to crops grown with ridges and furrows.

      v) This method is suitable for crops *i.e.* Sorghum, cotton, maize, tobacco, potato, sugarcane etc.

6.   Surge Method

      i) **Intermittent application of water** to the field surface under gravity flow which results in a series of "**On and Off**" modes of constant or variable time spans.

Advantages

      i) Infiltration uniformity is increased,

      ii) Deep percolation is reduced compared to continuous water application due to intermittent wetting and dewatering process.

B) Sub Surface Irrigation Method

      i) Through under ground perforated pipes or through deep trenches at 15-30 m. intervals water gradually wet root zone through capillary movement.

Advantages

      i) Evaporation loss is less due to dry surface

      ii) Less weed management

      iii) Deep trenches should be made for drainage.

Disadvantages

      i) Deep percolation through trenches.

      ii) Maintenance of pipe lines is difficult

      iii) High initial cost

C) Micro Irrigation Methods

      1. Sprinkler Irrigation

      2. Drip Irrigation

1.   Sprinkler Irrigation

      i) Water is applied as spray or as rain over the crop.

      ii) Rate of water delivery is > 1000 litre/hrs.

      iii) It operates at the pressure of > 2.5 bar and through water as a spray upto the distance of >10 m.

Advantages

      i) Uniform distribution of water,

      ii) Saving of water from 25-50 per cent,

      iii) Saving of land 10-20 per cent,

iv) Irrigation area is increased by 1-2 times with the same amount of the water,

v) No risk of runoff and erosion,

vi) Suitable for undulating land and steep sloppy,

vii) Suitable for areas where water and labour scarcity,

viii) Suitable for saline soils to leach salts.

Disadvantages

i) Not followed under high wing velocity (>12 km/hour),

ii) High initial costs,

iii) High energy is required (0.50 to >10 kg/cm^2),

iv) More spreading of diseases,

v) Can not be used for rice and jute crops.

2. Drip Irrigation

Discovered in Israel.

i) It is also known as **trickle irrigation**

ii) Discharge rate of water per dripper is 1-4 litre/hrs,

iii) It consists of main line, sub pipe line, laterals and emitters,

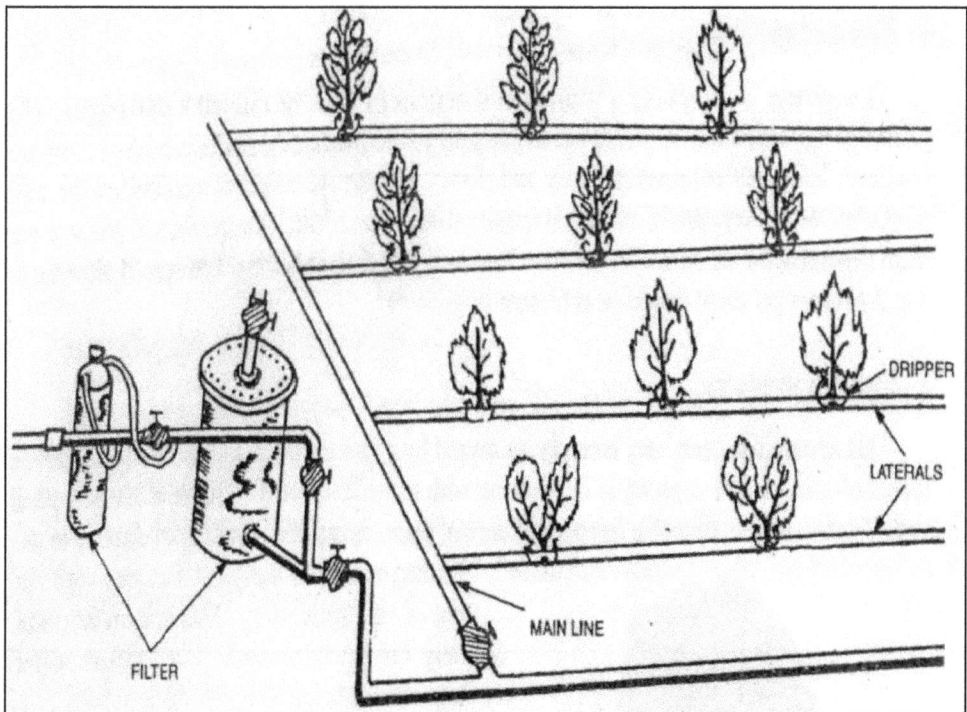

Drip Irrigation/Trickle Irrigation

iv) The discharge is from emitters,

v) The irrigation interval is 1-4 days,

vi) It saves 50-70 per cent water.

Advantages

i) Well suited for areas of acute water shortage,

ii) Minimization of soil erosion and deep percolation and runoff losses,

iii) Water is maintained at field capacity,

iv) Salt concentration is less,

v) No land levelling is necessary,

vi) Herbigation and Fertigation can also be applied,

vii) Less disease and weed infestation.

Disadvantages

i) Clogging of emitter,

ii) Damage to lateral systems due to rodents and other animals,

iii) Salt accumulation near plants due to lack of sufficient moisture for leaching,

iv) High initial cost,

v) Most suitable for wider spaced orchard crops and sugarcane,

vi) Inadequate root development.

COMPARATIVE STUDY BETWEEN SPRINKLER AND DRIP IRRIGATION

Sl.No.	Particulars		Sprinkler Irrigation	Drip Irrigation
1.	Form of water	:	Spray or rain	Drop
2.	Rate of delivery	:	> 1000 litre/hrs	1-4 litre/hr
3.	Water saves	:	25-50 per cent	60-70 per cent
4.	Land saving	:	10-16 per cent	-
5.	Uniformity	:	Uniform application of water (up to10 m)	Root zone application
6.	Suitable for	:	Undulating land, sandy soil, areas where water and labour scarcity is common, saline soil	Wider spaced crop. orchard and vegetable garden, areas where acute water shortage
7.	Not used under	:	High wind velocity	Efficient and technical labour scarcity

Fertigation

☆ Fertigation is the application of fertilizers, soil amendments and other water-soluble products required by the plant during its growth stages through drip/sprinkler irrigation system.

☆ Fertigation is a method of fertilizer application in which fertilizer is incorporated within the irrigation water by the drip system.

☆ In this system, fertilizer solution is distributed evenly in irrigation. The availability of nutrients is very high therefore the efficiency is more.

☆ In this method, liquid fertilizer as well as water soluble fertilizers is used.

☆ Nitrogen and sulphur are the principle nutrients applied by Fertigation.

Advantages of Fertigation

1. Nutrient and water are supplied near the active root zone through fertigation which results in greater absorption by the crops.

2. As water and fertilizer are supplied uniformly to all the crops through fertigation, there is possibility for getting 25-50 per cent higher yield.

3. Fertilizer use efficiency through fertigation ranges between 80-90 per cent, which helps to save a minimum of 25 per cent of nutrients.

4. By this way, along with less amount of water and saving of fertilizer, time, labour and energy use is also reduced substantially.

☆ Urea, potash, sulphur, micro-nutrients and other highly water soluble fertilizers are applied through fertigation in solution form as per plant requirements.

(G) Post Harvest Practices of Horticultural Crops

☆ Post harvest technology/post harvest management may be defined as the branch of agriculture that deals with all the operations right from harvesting or even the pre-harvest stages till the commodity reaches the consumer, either in fresh (grains, apple, mango, tomato fruits) or processed form (flour, juice, nectar, ketchup) and utilization of the wastes (peel, seed, skin etc.) in a profitable manner (manufacture of fermented beverages, colour extraction, pectin extraction etc.).

Importance of Post Harvest Technology

1. **Reduction in post harvest losses:** Post harvest technology ensures reduction of losses in what has already been produced. So, reduction of post harvest losses is an alternative way of increasing production of agricultural and horticultural crops.

2. **Reduction of cost of production:** Post harvest technology reduces cost of production, packaging, storage, transportation, marketing and distribution, lowers the price for the consumer and increases the farmer's income.

3. **Reducing malnutrition:** Proper post harvest technology ensures availability of sufficient food to all thus reducing malnutrition and ensuring healthy growth of the nation. It also extends the season of availability of a particular commodity.

4. **Economic loss reduction:** Reduces economic losses at grower level, during marketing and at consumers end.

5. **Availability:** Had there been no knowledge of post harvest technology, apples would not have ever reached Kerala and Banana in H.P. or Kashmir today. Today we can get perishable commodities like Banana, tomato etc. throughout the year and in almost every place in the country. Apples can be made available through out the year although the cropping season is just for 2-3 months. Thanks to the advancement made in the field of post harvest technology. The increasing exports of fruits and vegetables have become possible only by the interventions made in post harvest technology.

6. **Employment generation:** The food processing industry ranks first in terms of employment generation with approximately 15 lakhs persons employed. Employment potential in post harvest and value addition sector is considered to be very high. Every one crore rupee invested in fruit and vegetable processing in the organized sector generates 140 persons per year of employment as compared to just 1050 person days of employment per year in small scale investment (SSI) units. The SSI unit in food industry employs 4,80,000 persons, contributing 13 per cent of all SSI units employed.

7. **Export earnings:** Export of fresh and processed horticultural commodities also attracts valuable foreign exchange.

8. **Defense and astronaut's requirements:** Defense forces posted in remote border areas as well as astronauts who travel into space have special requirements of ready to eat and high energy low volume food. The requirements are fulfilled by processing industries.

9. **Infant and sports preparations:** To day special infant and sports drinks and other processed preparations are available for use especially by these people. These preparations are done especially to meet the specific nutritional requirements of their body.

Post Harvest Handling

Post harvest handling is the name given to all the processes through which the fruits and vegetables pass from the time of harvest till they are delivered to the consumer.

1) **Pre-cooling:** High temperatures are detrimental to keeping quality of fruits and vegetables especially when harvesting is done during hot days. Pre-cooling is a means of removing field heat. It slows down the respiration of the produce, minimizes susceptibility to attack of micro-organisms, reduces water loss and eases the load on cooling system of storage or transport. Currently used pre-cooling methods include room cooling, forced air cooling, water cooling, vacuum cooling and package icing.

2) **Curing:** It is done immediately after harvesting. It strengthens the skin. The process is induced at a relatively higher temperature and humidity involving sterilization of outer tissues followed by the development of wound periderm which acts as an effective barrier against infection and water loss. It is favoured by high temperature and high humidity. Potato, sweet potato, colocasia, onion, garlic are cured prior to storage or marketing. In Sweet potato this condition is most rapid at 33°C and relative humidity of 95 per cent. Potato tubers are held at 18°C for 2 days and then at 7–10°C for 10-12 days at 90 per cent relative humidity. Curing also reduces the moisture content especially in onion and garlic. Drying of superficial leaves of onion bulbs protects them from microbial infection in storage. Maximum safe temperature for onion curing at field is 37.8°C for 3-5 days. Artificial curing of onions in crates at 40°C for 16 hours reduces rot losses in storage.

3) **De-greening:** It is the process of decomposing green pigments in fruits usually by applying ethylene or other similar metabolic inducers to give a fruit its characteristic colour as preferred by the consumer. It is applicable to banana, mango, citrus and tomato. The time required to degreen a fruit depends upon the degree of natural colour break at maturity. The higher the green colour and more mature a fruit is, the less time is required to reduce the chlorophyll to a desired level. De-greening is carried out in special treating rooms with controlled temperature and humidity in which low concentrations ethylene (20ppm) is applied to keep the CO_2 level below 1 per cent (Low colouring). The ethylene should be supplied from a gas cylinder. These rooms are thoroughly ventilated to keep the carbon-dioxide level below 1 per cent, which does not allow higher colouring. Ethylene accelerates decomposition of chlorophyll with out significantly affecting the synthesis of carotenoid pigments. The best degreening temperature is 27°C. Higher temperature delay degreening. The Relative humidity should be 85-90 per cent.Higher humidity levels cause condensation during degreening and are associated with slow degreening and increase in decay. Low humidity though checks decay causes excessive shrinkage, shriveling and peel break down.

4) **Washing and drying:** Most of the fruits and vegetables are washed after harvesting to improve their appearance, prevent wilting and remove primary inoculum load of micro organisms. Hence fungicide or bactericide should be used in washing water. Washing improves shelf life of bananas by delaying their ripening. After washing excess of water should be removed this would otherwise encourage microbial spoilage. Root and tuber crops are often washed to remove the soil adhering to them.

5) **Sorting and grading:** Immature, diseased and badly bruised fruits and vegetables are sorted out. Most of the countries have their own set of standards of domestic trade and for international trade standards have also been defined. Grades are based on size, weight, colour and shape. Grading is done manually or mechanically.

6) **Dis-infestation**: Papaya, mango, melon and other fruits are susceptible to fruit fly attacks. Dis-infestation is done either by vapour heat treatment at 43°C with air saturated with water vapour for 6-8 hours, by ethylene dibromide fumigation (18-22g of EDB/cubic meter for 2-4 hours. Residues of inorganic bromide must not exceed 10Vg/g) or by cold treatment (exposure of fruits to near freezing temperature for a specified period).

7) **Post harvest treatments**: Post harvest application of Bavistin (0.1 per cent) and topsin (0.1 per cent) controls storage diseases in mango. In Nagpur mandarins, hot water treatment with Imazalil (0.1 per cent), Bavistin (0.1 per cent) and Benlate (0.1 per cent) is most effective. A complete inhibition of sprouting of cool chamber (evaporatively cooled) stored potatoes for 4 months and 5 months is achieved by spraying them with an aqueous emulsion of CIPC @ 50mg and 100 mg/kg of tubers respectively before completion of dormancy period.

8) **Waxing**: Fruits and vegetables have a natural waxy layer on their outer surface which is partly removed by waxing. An extra layer of wax is applied artificially with sufficient thickness and consistency to prevent an aerobic condition with in the fruits provides necessary protection against decay organisms. Waxing is especially important if tiny injuries and scratches on their surface are present. These can be sealed by wax. Waxing also enhances the glossiness of fruits or vegetables. Therefore, appearance is improved making them more acceptable. If refrigerated storage facilities are not available, protective skin coating with wax increases the storage life of fresh fruits and vegetables at ambient temperature.

9) **Control of ripening process:** Ripening transforms a physically mature but inedible plant organ in to a visually attractive taste and smell sensation. It marks the completion of development and commencement of senescence with the life of a fruit and is normally an irreversible event. For ripening adequate quantity of ethylene should be used in the ripening room at regular intervals. A concentration of CO_2 above 1 per cent delays ripening. Hence, thorough ventilation is necessary. By use of ethephon commercially known as ethrel, making it alkaline using caustic soda (3 g of soda for 20ml of ethephon).Calcium carbide can also be used for ripening (100g for 100kg of fruits). Ripening in fruits and vegetables can be retarded by using proper packaging, low temperature, ethylene absorbents, skin coating of waxol, growth retardants and using fungicides for controlling their spoilage.

10) **Pre-packaging in plastic films:** This increases shelf-life by creating a modified atmosphere with an increase in concentration of CO_2 in the package. The packaging material should provide reasonable access to oxygen. For this, breathing film like polyesterine and cellulose acetate are used. But tougher LDPE films which have high O_2 and CO_2 transmission rates are more durable. The pouches must have perforations to transmit O_2 and CO_2 rapidly enough for the respiration of fresh produce. The pouches used reduce bruising, facilitates inspection, reduces moisture loss (weight loss) and prevents dehydration. It also creates modified atmosphere.

11) **Palletization:** Pallets are widely used for the transport of fruit and vegetable packages, in all developed countries. Loading and unloading are very important steps in the post harvest handling of fruits and vegetables but are often neglected. Loading and unloading are done manually in India. Due to low unit load there is a tendency to throw, drop or mishandle the package damaging the commodity. This loss can be considerably reduced by using pallet system. However; this requires the standardization of box dimensions. For each commodity it should be worked out. Once this is accomplished, mechanical loading and unloading become very easy with the fork lift system.

12) **Irradiation:** Application of irradiation for suppressing sprouting and hence extension of shelf life has been allowed in India. Sprouting onion can be checked by gamma irradiation at a dose of 0.06-0.1 KGY. In potato gamma irradiation at 0.1 KGY can inhibit sprouting completely. The irradiated potatoes could be stored successfully for 6 months at 15°C with 10 per cent loss. Irradiation in Banana, Guava, Mango and Papaya improves shelf-life due to delay in rate of ripening and senescence.

(H) Management of Orchards

Establishment of an Orchard

Establishment of an orchard is a long term investment and deserves very careful planning. The selection of proper location and site, planting system and planting distance, choosing the varieties and the nursery plants have to be considered carefully to ensure maximum production.

Criteria for Selection of Site

The following factors are to be considered before selecting a site for an orchard.

1) **Climate:** The climate of the locality should be suited to the fruits, or the fruit chosen should be suited to the climate. Enquiries should be made on the following points to assess how climate affects the fruits intended to be grown.

   A. Experience of the fruit growers and research stations in the locality regarding the acclimatization of the fruits under consideration.

   B. The seasons of heavy rainfall, hail storms and hot winds.

   C. The seasons and intervals of cyclones, heat waves, gales and other catastrophic features

2) **Soil:** Few prospective sites should be examined for both physical and chemical properties. For this purpose profile pits of 2m depth should be dug in each representative part of the site as suggested by external appearance, Samples should be collected and analyzed for deciding the choice. Soil samples must be analyzed to know the suitability of soil for growing fruit crops. Soil analysis gives information on the type of soil, its fertility; its pH value etc. As far as possible flat land should be selected.There should be no hard pan up to a depth of 2m.

3) **Irrigation facilities:** Most of the horticulture crops are raised under irrigation. So the water facilities should also be taken in to consideration (quantity and quality).Water table should be below 2 m depth.

4) **Nearness to the market:** Saves the over head charges in transport and gives close touch with market tastes (in the case of market gardens).In most cases a large percentage of the retail price of fruits is accounted for by transport charges. The hill bananas and the apples of Kulu valley are produced cheap but they are sold at high prices on the plains owing to heavy cost of transport.

5) **Transport facilities:** Fruits being perishable cannot be moved for long distances with out quick and refrigerated transport. Bananas from the south are not reaching northern market in our own country owing to the absence of refrigerated transport. But under refrigerated conditions, they can be transported to longer distances. So, the orchards must be located where there is quick transport, preferably a refrigerated transport system.

6) **Power (electricity) supply:** It would be a great advantage if electric power lines are running in the proximity of the area as it can be tapped easily.

7) **Proximity to established orchards:** It is an added advantage if the site is in proximity to the already established orchards because of compactness of areas of production facilitates provision of transport and storage facilities. It also enables formation of co-operative societies and other associations which can collectively own grading and spraying machinery and other costly equipment including storage facilities. If there are compact blocks of single crop say citrus, banana, mango etc. the spread of diseases and pests are more. In selecting a site close to other orchards, one must make sure that they are free from devastating pests and diseases like citrus scale, canker, panama disease of banana, the tristeza disease of citrus.

8) **Availability of labour:** Large orchards are started often in out of the way places and forest areas away from populated centres. It would therefore be necessary to ensure that adequate labour is available for orchard operations. This point is of important in plantation crops particularly.

9) **Social factors:** These assume importance when large contingents of labour and managerial staff are to be employed as plantations or large orchards. They should be provided with medical and educational facilities, so that, they are content and stick on to the jobs.

10) **Presence of nurseries close by:** It is an advantage if the nurseries are close by to the selected site for selecting the plants for the orchard after studying the scion parents personally. It will also help to get cheap and quick transport of plants which will ensure better establishment.

11) **Cost of the land:** Cost of the land comes up for consideration when all the other requirements listed above have been satisfied. It should never be the prime consideration in the choice a little extra cost paid for the foregoing amenities is more than repaid in the long run.

Orchard Plan

It is of great advantage to prepare a plan of the orchard in advance, be it a home or market garden or a commercial orchard. A detailed survey of the site is carried out including the levels and a good map to scale is drawn. A full knowledge of the fruits to be grown and their cultivation is also prerequisite for efficient planning.

The general principles should be considered while preparing the plan:

1. If the entire area is not of the same type of soil, each fruit should be allocated to the soil type it prefers.

2. The irrigation sources should be marked and channels indicated along gradients with a view to achieve most economical conduct of water.

3. Irrigated fruits should be close to the source of irrigation to avoid long irrigation channels and consequent loss of water during conduct.

4. Tall wind breaks should be planted especially on the sides from which high winds are expected. There should be adequate clearance between the wind breaks and the crop.

5. Roads should be planned to occupy the minimum space consistent with economy of transport of orchard requisites and produce. The space between the wind break and the first row of fruit trees may often be utilized for roads and canals etc. with advantages.

6. Drains should follow the gradient of the land, should be as straight as possible and concealed from the visitors, if possible.

7. When varieties with pollen preferences are planted they should have the pollenizer in an adjacent block or in alternate rows so as to ensure good crop set.

8. Fruits which ripen at the same time should preferably be grouped together to facilitate easy watching and harvesting.

9. Assign rear areas for tall trees and the front for shorter ones will besides facilitating watching, also improves the appearance of the orchard. The orchard should in general present an aesthetic appearance so as to provide marked attraction.

10. The spacing adopted should be the optimum. The spacing allowed is usually such that the fringes of the trees will just touch one another cutting out light but should not interlock.

11. With in reasonable limits, closer spacing gives more yields in the earlier age. But in later life, the trees tend to grow taller than broad resulting in difficulty in pruning, spraying and harvesting. They also suffer from root competition inadequate nutrition, fewer fruits which tend to be smaller with comparatively poorer in colour development. So, adoption of closer spacing to accommodate more plants per acre proves to be a false economy in the long run. The spacing given to fruit plants depends on the following factors:

a) The habit of growth of the plant: The spacing being equal to the spread of the plants.

b) Rainfall: In the case of rain fed crops closer spacing is given in lighter rainfall areas than in heavy rainfall areas.

c) Nature of soil: Trees on stiffer soils may be given less spacing as both their top and root spread are limited in such soils.

d) The root stock: Root stock influences the spread of the trees and to that extent determines the spacing to be adopted.

e) Pruning and training

f) Irrigation system.

g) The method of layout should be fixed in advance so that the no. of plants required is worked out and arranged for.

Steps in Establishment of an Orchard

After the selection of the site and drafting the plan, next comes the establishment of an orchard with fruit plants. For this, the selected site should be thoroughly surveyed for studying its size, topography, flow of irrigation water, drainage and fertility gradients. The positioning of main and subsidiary roads, wells, wind breaks etc. should be planned clearly.

Steps

1. **Clearing of the land:** Preparation of the soil depends largely on its condition, previous history and grower's plans. If the land has been under cultivation and has been well maintained, nothing further may be required. On the other hand if the site is a new one and was never under cultivation earlier, much has to be done well in advance for planting. If the land is a virgin land *i.e.* it is not under cultivation previously, the existing vegetation is to be cleared. Standing trees, shrubs, bushes etc. should be cut down and uprooted along with the stumps and removed. No vegetation should be left on the site. Otherwise, they may shade the young plants; compete for water, light and nutrients. Further, their removal at a later date is expensive and risky. All the stumps and roots may be removed. Otherwise they may harbour white ants, termite hills, diseases etc. and spread to the new plants. Along with vegetation, stones, rocks and ant hills, termite hills etc. should be removed.

2. **Leveling:** Leveling is important for efficient irrigation, drainage to check soil erosion and also for improving appearance. If the land is sloppy contouring (if the slope is 3 to 10 per cent) or terracing (if the slope is >10 per cent) is to be done. During levelling sub soil should not be exposed.

3. **Fencing:** Fencing is necessary to protect trees from stray cattle, human trespassing and also for attractiveness. The fence may be of stone, barbed wire or live fence. Growing of live fence is an expensive one. At the initial stage it may be cheap but afterwards the maintenance is costly. Live fence

needs periodical punning or trimming to shape and also to control their growth and encouraging more branching. This is one of the costly items of the orchard cultivation.

Examples of **non-thorny fence plants**: Tamarind, Thevitia, Lawsonia, Casuarina, Gliricidia etc.

Examples of **thorny fence plants**: Agave, Cactus, Prosophis, Commiphora *barli, Inga dulcis* etc.

4. **Wind break plants:** The wind breaks are provided to resist the velocity of wind which causes loss of bloom, wind erosion and evaporation of moisture and to keep the orchard warm by checking frost and cold waves. The beneficial effect of wind break is felt up to a distance equal to 3 times its height.

5. **Roads and drains:** These are laid out according to the plan prepared in advance taking the convenience and levels into consideration. Main irrigation channels also have to be plotted. Open drains should be straight, running parallel to the gradient. Silt catching devices should be employed in the drains. Covered drains should be filled with big stones at the base and smaller ones over them and the top 12 inches should be covered with the orchard soil so as not to impede ploughing and other operations.

6. **Tillage:** Tillage including sub soil should be done thoroughly at this stage, since it cannot be done after planting without disturbing the roots of the trees.

7. **Sowing green manure crops:** A green manure crop is sown thick and uniformly all over the area to be planted. Apart from the manurial value the crop reveals by its growth, infertile patches of the land, so that they can be examined and suitable steps are taken for amending them.

8. **Marking plant positions:** The system of layout should be decided first. Then one of the fence lines or a road should be chosen as the base line. In deciding the base line, due regard should be given to appearance of the rows from the road along which the visitor or the manager is expected to walk.

9. **Digging and filling of pits:** Generally the pits are dug 2 to 3 months in advance of planting *i.e.* March to May. Allow the pits to weather. A planting board (a plank about 1.5m long or longer with two end notches and a center notch) is applied to the marking peg by its central notch and two pegs are driven at the end notches. Then the board and the marking pegs are removed and a pit of 1-meter cube is dug. The two pegs driven at the end notches remain in position on either side of the pit. All pits are dug similarly so that plant position is not altered at planting time. While digging, the topsoil should be kept on one side and the bottom soil on another side separately as the top soil is somewhat fertile than the bottom soil. While filling the pits, the topsoil is mixed with farmyard manure or compost, leaf mould or green leaf and a kilogram of super phosphate. Then the pits are

filled with the bottom layer of soil first and then with the topsoil mixed with the manures. The soil after filling should rise about a foot over the orchard level so as to allow for shrinkage on setting.

10. **Filling of pits:** Filling is done a fortnight or two after digging pits. The pits are filled with a mixture of Top soil; FYM, leaf mould and bone meal. Pits are filled a few inches above the ground level for shrinkage and settlement.

11. **Selection of plants from the nursery:** Generally the plants are purchased from the nursery well in advance. The grower should visit the nursery and select the plants. Plants are selected on the basis of certain characters of the plants.

   A. **Branching:** The main branches on the young plants become leaders on a grown up tree. The branches on the trunk should not be opposite or in a whorl but alternate with at least 15cm spacing.

   B. **Growth of the plant:** The plants should be uniform in growth and is determined by uniform length of internodes.

   C. **Age of the plants:** Growers generally prefer older plants believing that these plants come to bearing early.

   D. **Pests and diseases:** Plants should be free from pests and diseases like scale insects, mealy bugs, aphids, nematodes etc and diseases like canker, and viral diseases.

12. **Lifting and packing:** Before lifting of plants from the nursery the nursery is thoroughly irrigated one day in advance for easy lifting of the plants without damage to the root system. Then the plants are lifted carefully along with a ball of earth attached to the root system. The roots are wrapped in straw or grass or covered with a gunny cloth and placed in a basket or a wooden crate for packing. Depending on the size of the basket or crate 6-7 plants are kept for each basket.4-5 long bamboo splinter or wooden pegs are forked into the sides of the basket and tied at the top. In between the plants and at the top of the basket after filling, the plants recovered with straw so as to avoid falling during transit.

13. **Season of planting:** The distribution of rainfall in the tropics and subtropics and the break of spring growth in temperate zone determine the season of planting. In tropical climate, most trees are planted between July and December and few in January also. In general planting is done during the monsoon in moderate rainfall areas and at the close of the monsoon in heavy rainfall areas. Planting should be done on cloudy days and preferably in the afternoons rather than in the morning.

14. **Planting:** The planting board should be used at the time of setting the plants, so that they are in a perfect line. The plants should be set in the soil to the same level as it was in the nursery. The bud/graft joint should not be covered with soil. Plants should be irrigated once copiously to get the soil particles to closely adhere to the roots and also to drive away the air around the roots completely. The plants should be staked with a straight bamboo

piece or other twig. Graft bandage should be removed if not already done. Any buds on the rootstocks should be rubbed off.

15. **Heeling inn:** If the plants after transport are not directly planted in the field, they may be kept in shade in a slanting position along the side of a trench moistening the ball of earth.They may be left in this position till active growth commences by which time they should be planted in the field. This process is known as healing inn.

(I) Extraction and Storage of Vegetable (Tomato) Seeds

Methods of Extraction of Tomato Seed

1. **Alkali method:** Best and safest method, Seed slurry treated with 10 per cent washing soda (Ca. carbonate) and kept for overnight.

2. **Fermentation method:** Ripe fruits are crushed and then kept for 2-4 days at 15-24°C.

3. **Acid fermentation method:** 250 ml of HCl is treated with 10 ml of seed slurry and kept for 30 minutes.

Storage Conditions

	Mature Green	*Pink*	*Ripe*
Temperature:	13–18°C	10–13°C	7–10°C
Relative Humidity:	85–90 per cent	-Same-	-Same-
Storage Period:	2–3 weeks	7–10 days	3–5 days

Chapter 4

Differentiation Between Agricultural Terms

(A) Soil Fertility and Soil Productivity

Soil Fertility	*Soil Productivity*
1. It is considered as an index of available nutrients to plants	1. It is a broader term used to indicate yields of crops.
2. It is one of the factors for crop production. The other factors are water supply, slope of the land, depth of water table etc.	2. It is the interaction of all the factors that determine the magnitude of yields.
3. It can be analysed in the laboratory	3. It can be assessed in the field under particular climatic conditions.
4. It is the potential status of the soil.	4. It is the resultant of various factors soil factors influencing soil management to produce crops.
5. Organic matter in the soil improves soil fertility by mineralization of nutrients.	5. Organic matter also improves soil productivity by improving soil porosity, aggregation and physical condition of soil thus modifying the soil environment for crop growth.

(B) Acid Soil and Saline Soil

Acid Soil	Saline Soil
1. The soils with pH less than 6.5	1. Saline soil have soil pH of more than 6.5 but less than 8.5
2. Low in Ca, Mg with negligible amount of soluble salts	2. Dominated by sulphate and chloride ions and low in exchangeable sodium
3. This soils appear as brown or reddish brown	3. It has white colour that why it is also called as *White alkali*.
4. Lime is added in soil to neutralize acidity and to increase the pH, so that the availability of nutrients will be increased	4. Gypsum and Pyrite is added. Sulphur present in both causes decrease in pH of soil due to formation of H_2SO_4
5. Calcium Ammonium Nitrate (CAN) is suitable to acidic soils.	5. Super phosphate, Ammonium sulphate or Urea fertilizers can be applied in saline soils. MOP and Ammonium chlorides should not be used.

(C) Saline Soil and Alkaline Soil

Saline Soil	Alkaline Soil
1. This soil is known as Solan chalk.	1. This soil is known as Solanetz.
2. The soluble salt concentration is ≥ 0.1 per cent	2. The soluble salt concentration is < 0.1 per cent
3. It has white colour that why also called as *White alkali*.	3. It has Black colour that why called as *Black alkali*.
4. Presence of Cl^- and SO_4^{2-} ions of Na^+	4. Presence of CO_3^{2-} ions of Na^+

(D) Intercropping and Mixed Cropping

Intercropping	Mixed Cropping
1. Crops are sown in different rows without affecting the population of main crop when sown as sole crop.	1. Either sown in rows or mixed without considering the population of either
2. The main object is to utilize the space left between two rows of main crop.	2. To get at least one crop under favourable conditions is the object.

Intercropping	Mixed Cropping
3. More emphasis is given to the main crop.	3. All crops are cared equally
4. There is no competition between both crops.	4. There is competition between all crops growing
5. Inter crops are of short duration and are harvested much earlier than main.	5. The crops are almost of the same duration
6. Sowing time may be same or different.	6. It is same for all crops.

(E) Intercropping and Relay Cropping

Intercropping	Relay Cropping
1. Crops are sown in different rows without affecting the population of main crop when sown as sole crop. *e.g.* Sowing of Potato in between row of Sugarcane.	1. Inter planting or inter sowing of seeds/seedlings of the succeeding crop before harvesting the preceding/maturing crop. *e.g.* sowing of Lathyrus or Lentil before the harvest of rice in lowland area.
2. The main object is to utilize the space left between two rows of main crop.	2. An objective to use the residual moisture of rice field
3. It creates obstruction in the free use of machines for intercultural operations	3. It does not.
4. Separate yield of both crops decrease because of adverse competition effect.	4. Yield of both crops are not affected because of zero competition.

(F) Mixed Farming and Mixed Cropping

Mixed Farming	Mixed Cropping
1. A system of farming on a particular farm which includes crop production, raising livestock, poultry, fisheries, bee keeping etc. to sustain and safety as many needs of the farmer as possible.	1. Cultivation of two or more than two crops simultaneously on the same piece of land without any definite row pattern or fixed ratio.
2. Main objective is subsistence while higher profitability without altering ecological balance	2. Main objective is to lessen the risk of total crop failure and to satisfy the farmers in food and fodder
3. Cropping pattern which involve the raising of crops, animals and or trees	3. Cropping pattern which involve the raising of only crops of same season.

(G) Weather and Climate

Weather	Climate
1. It is defined as "A state or condition of the atmosphere at a given place and at a given instant of time".	1. "The generalised weather or summation of weather conditions over a given region during comparatively longer period".
2. Changes from place to place even in a small locality	2. Different in different large regions
3. Changes according to time (every moment)	3. Change requires longer (years) time
4. Crop growth, development and yield are decided by weather in a given season	4. Selection of crops suitable for a place is decided based on climate of the region
5. Under aberrant weather conditions planners can adopt a short-term contingent planning.	5. Helps in long-term agricultural planning.

(H) Pruning and Training

Pruning	Training
1. Training is originated by the observation that the branches horizontally disposed bear more fruit than the vertical one which are sky to bearing likewise the upper branches bear more fruit than the lower ones.	1. Pruning is originated by the observation that simple disposition of the branches in a particular position is not sufficient to achieve be crop but a definite fruits are exists on the plants towards which if sap flows as divert to plant bears as abundantly and superior quality.
2. Training is mainly concerned with giving a frame and shape to the plant.	2. Pruning has an effect on the function of plant as it influences cropping of plant highly.
3. Training determines the general character and even details of plant out line its branching and frame work.	3. Pruning determines the capacity of plant to produce fruit.
4. By training we can keep the plant or vine in a manageable shape and can dispose the branches in desirable direction and position.	4. By pruning we can actually drive the flow of sap towards fruiting area on plant and force the plant or vine bear better quality of fruits *e.g.* Grape.

(I) Grafting and Budding

Grafting	Budding
1. It is a technique in which a section of a stem with leaf buds is inserted into the stock of a tree. The upper part of the graft (the scion) becomes the top of the plant; the lower portion (the rootstock) becomes the root system or part of the trunk.	1. A method of grafting in which the scion (upper portion of the graft) is a single bud rather than a piece of stem or twig.
2. This propagation technique is slower than budding.	2. This is faster than any other grafting technique.
3. The percentage of success is much lower.	3. The percentage of successful unions is usually greater.

(J) Irrigation and Fertigation

Irrigation	Fertigation
1. Irrigation is the artificial application of water for the purpose of supplying moisture essential to plant growth.	1. Fertigation is the application of fertilizer with irrigation water in either open or closed system. Sprinkler and drip systems are the main closed systems.
2. With the security of cropping under irrigation, additional inputs (tillage, fertilizers, plant protection etc.) become economically feasible.	2. Nitrogen and sulphur are the principle nutrients applied by fertigation.
3. Irrigation can prolong the effective growing period in areas with dry seasons, plant permitting multiple cropping and employment generation.	3. This saves the application cost and allows the utilization of relatively in expensive water-soluble fertilizers.

Chapter 5

Role of Agricultural Engineering in Agriculture

Mechanisation plays very important role in the field of Agriculture. The timeliness of operation with an ease and judicious use of inputs are the important parameters for increased production. Use of improved Agricultural equipments can increase crop production by 15-20 per cent. Intensive cultivation is only possible by using the newly developed farm-Machineries.

Agricultural engineering is the discipline that applies engineering science and technology to agricultural production and processing. Agricultural engineering combines the disciplines of animal biology, plant biology, and mechanical, civil, electrical and chemical engineering principles with a knowledge of agricultural principles.

Important Role of Agricultural Engineering in Agriculture

1. Design of agricultural machinery, equipment, and agricultural structures,
2. Internal combustion engines as applied to agricultural machinery,
3. Agricultural resource management (including land use and water use),
4. Water management, conservation, and storage for crop irrigation and livestock production,
5. Surveying and land profiling,
6. Climatology and atmospheric science,
7. Soil management and conservation, including erosion and erosion control,
8. Seeding, tillage, harvesting, and processing of crops,
9. Livestock production, including poultry, fish, and dairy animals,

10. Waste management, including animal waste, agricultural residues, and fertilizer runoff,

11. Food engineering and the processing of agricultural products,

12. Physical and chemical properties of materials used in, or produced by, agricultural production,

13. Bioresource engineering, which uses machines on the molecular level to help the environment,

14. Design of experiments related to crop and animal production.

Agricultural engineers may perform tasks as planning, supervising and managing the building of dairy effluent schemes, irrigation, drainage, flood and water control systems, perform environmental impact assessments, agricultural product processing and interpret research results and implement relevant practices. Some work in industry, for manufacturers of agricultural machinery, equipment, processing technology, and structures for housing livestock and storing crops. Agricultural engineers work in production, sales, management, research and development, or applied science.

References

Arora, J.S. 2007. Introductory Ornamental Horticulture. Kalyani Publishers, Ludhiana, India.

Balasubramaniyan, P. and S.P. Palaniappan. 2002. Principles and Practices of Agronomy. Agrobios publishers, Jodhpur, India.

Biswas, T.D. and S.K. Mukherjee. 1989. A text book of Soil Science. Tata Mcgraw-Hill Publishing Co., New Delhi, India.

Chadha, K.L. 2006. Handbook of Horticulture. Publication of I.C.A.R., New Delhi, India.

Cheema, S.S., B.K. Dhaliwal and T.S. Sahota. 2006. Agronomy: Theory and Digest. Kalyani Publishers, Ludhiana, India.

Das, D.K. 1999. Introductory Soil Science. Kalyani Publishers, Ludhiana, India.

Gupta, O.P. 1998. Weed Management: Principles and Practices. Agro Botanica, Bikaner, India.

Gupta, S.N. and Naik, K.B. 2005. Instant Horticulture. Jain Brothers Publishers, New Delhi, India.

ICAR, 2010. Handbook of Agriculture. Indian Council of Agricultural Research, New Delhi, India.

Indian Horticulture Database, 2011. Ministry of Agriculture, Government of India, Gurgaon, India.

Katyayan, A. 2002. Fundamentals of Agriculture vol(1). Kushal Publications, Varanasi, India.

Katyayan, A. 2007. Fundamentals of Agriculture vol(2). Kushal Publications, Varanasi, India.

Maitry, R. S. 2010. Brief Book of Agriculture. Indian Agricultural Research Institute, New Delhi, India.

Maliwal, P.L. 2002. Agronomy - At a glance. Agrotech Publishing Academy, Udaipur, India.

Michael, A.M. 1978. Irrigation - Theory and Practices. Vikas Publishing House Pvt. Ltd., New Delhi, India.

Morachan, Y.B 1993. Crop Production and Management. Oxford and IBH Publishing Co. Pvt. Ltd., New Delhi, India.

Palaniappan, S.P. and K. Sivaraman. 1996. Cropping System in Tropics: Principles and Management. New Age International (P) Limited Publishers, New Delhi, India.

Radha Krishna Murthy, V. 2002. Basic Principles of Agricultural Meteorology. BSR Publications, Hyderabad, India.

Rajendra Prasad, 2005. Textbook of Field Crops Production. ICAR, New Delhi, India.

Reddy, S.R. 2004. Principles of Crop Production. Kalyani Publishers, Ludhiana, India.

Reddy, S.R. 2007. Irrigation Agronomy. Kalyani Publishers, Ludhiana, India.

Reddy, S.R. 2007. Principles of Agronomy. Kalyani Publishers, Ludhiana, India.

Reddy, T. Yellamanda and G.H. Sankaran Reddi. 2004. Principles of Agronomy. Kalyani Publishers, Ludhiana, India.

Salaria, S.K. 2004. Horticulture at a Glance. Jain Brothers Publications, New Delhi, India.

Sankaran Reddi, G.H. and T. Yellamanda Reddy. 2004. Efficient Use of Irrigation Water. Kalyani Publishers, Ludhiana, India.

Sharma, R.K., *et.al*. 2011. Agriculture at a Glance. Daya Publishing House, New Delhi, India.

Sharma, R.K., N. Pandey, A.P. Singh and R.S. Maitry. 2011. Guide for Agricultural Entrance Examinations. Daya Publishing House, New Delhi, India.

Singh, A.P., T. Chowdhury and S. Gupta. 2010. Handbook of Weeds of Chhattisgarh. Yugbodh Publishers, Raipur, India.

Singh, Jitendra. 2008. Basic Horticulture. Kalyani Publishers, Ludhiana, India.

Singh, Mahendra. 2004. A Hand Book of Agriculture. Kalyani Publishers, Ludhiana, India.

Singh, S.S. 2006. Principles and Practices of Agronomy. Kalyani Publishers, Ludhiana, India.

Tisdale, S.L., W.L. Nelson, J.D. Beaton and J.L. Havlin. 1997. Soil Fertility and Fertilizers (V Edition). Prentice Hall of India Private Ltd., New Delhi, India.

Wakchaure, Goraksha. 2006. Agricultural Engineering (Notes). Indian Agricultural Research Institute, New Delhi. India.

Yawalkar, K.S., J.P. Agrawal and S. Bokde. 1984. Manures and Fertilizers. Agri-Horticulture Publishing House, Nagpur, India.

www.ingramcontent.com/pod-product-compliance
Lightning Source LLC
Chambersburg PA
CBHW020219290326
41948CB00001B/98